HUMAN PERFORMANCE AND SCUBA DIVING

Proceedings of the Symposium on Underwater Physiology

Scripps Institution of Oceanography
La Jolla, California
April 10-11, 1970

Cy Yttri
Director of Publications

Library of Congress
Catalog Card Number 77-142264

The Athletic Institute SBN 87670-805-X Chicago

FOREWORD

The sea is the next great frontier to be explored. Man, the ever inquisitive animal, has explored the Earth's land masses. Some men have ventured into the oceans to delve their secrets. "Hard hat" divers have been supplanted by SCUBA divers for many work tasks. Recreational SCUBA divers are increasing in numbers annually. Equipment—wet and dry suits, air tanks, regulators, face masks, flippers—is being supplied in ever increasing amounts.

SCUBA diving has been glamorized by television shows and popular magazine articles. The glamour of finding treasure in ancient wrecks has made many a Walter Mitty feel that he should become a diver. Too many people are unaware of both the physiological and psychological problems involved in working and playing in the ocean.

The Athletic Institute suggested to Scripps Institution of Oceanography that because Scripps had been instrumental in conducting SEALAB II in conjunction with the U. S. Navy, and because Scripps had so much knowledge of the problems involved in living, working and playing underwater, that a jointly sponsored symposium would be of value to both current and future SCUBA divers. Happily, Dr. William Nieremberg, Director of Scripps Institution of Oceanography, agreed. Dr. Nieremberg made available services of some of his staff to aid in planning and staging the symposium. The facilities at Scripps proved ideal for both the discussions and recreational aspects of the conference.

A steering committee planned the general format of the two-day meeting. The publication HUMAN PERFORMANCE AND SCUBA DIVING relates the outcome of that planning. It is my privilege to say to that group a heartfelt 'Thanks for a great job!". Dr. Glen Egstrom, UCLA; Jim Stewart, Scripps Institution of Oceanography; Dr. Ted Forbes, University of California, San Diego; Dr. Edmund Bernauer, University of California, Davis and Charles Jehle, AMF Voit Company, worked diligently to plan and stage the symposium. Glen Egstrom and Jim Stewart outdid themselves in obtaining speakers and reactors. Ted Forbes and his staff at UC, San Diego, did yeoman service in implementing the plans. Dr. Hugh Bradner, Scripps Institution, served as General Chairman of the actual sessions. Altogether, it took the efforts of many people to conduct this outstanding symposium.

The Athletic Institute is very grateful that so many highly qualified experts gave of their time and knowledge so that more and more people might become aware of the mechanical, physiological and psychological problems of SCUBA diving.

Frank B. Jones, President
The Athletic Institute

Table of Contents

Foreword III

Opening Address — Dr. Hugh Bradner — Symposium Chairman 1

First Session
- Effect of Diving Equipment on Diving Performance 3
  - Speaker — Dr. Glen H. Egstrom 5
  - Panelists — James R. Stewart 17
  - Bev B. Morgan 18
  - Lt. CDR Tommy Thompson 20
  - Discussion 21

Second Session
- Physiologic Processes as Applied to Problems of Living 33
  - Speaker — CDR Bob Hoke 35
  - Panelists — CDR Robert C. Bornmann 51
  - Lt. CDR Mark Bradley 63
  - CDR James Vorosmarti 70
  - Discussion 74

Third Session
- Diver Work Methods 81
  - Speaker — Dr. Gershon Weltman 83
  - Panelists — Dr. W. S. Vaughn, Jr. 102
  - Dr. Hugh A. Bowen 104
  - John T. Quirk 107
  - Discussion 109

Fourth Session
- Diving Behavior 117
  - Speaker — Dr. Arthur J. Bachrach 119
  - Panelists — Capt. Albert R. Behnke 139
  - Michael Greenwood 144
  - Dr. Joseph B. MacInnis 146
  - Discussion 150

Appendices
- Appendix from Technical Report R 653 (Diver Performance Using Handtools and Hand-held Pneumatic Tools) 155
- Speakers and Panelists 163
- Symposium Planning Committee 164
- Underwater Physiology Symposium Participants 164

OPENING ADDRESS

La Jolla, California
April 10-11, 1970

First Session
Dr. Hugh Bradner, Presiding

Dr. Bradner: I would like to open the Symposium with Dr. Fred Spiess, sometimes called Noel Spiess for fairly evident reasons, who started out as a theoretical plus experimental nuclear physicist under a Nobel Prize winner. He had the wisdom to abandon all that and come to Scripps to work in various oceanography. He is the Associate Director here. Without further ado Fred Spiess. Fred.

Dr. Spiess: It's a pleasure to welcome you here this morning and it's also a pleasure to have a rare, beautiful day to display to you. This is the kind of weather that people think we have all the time in La Jolla and really it is not quite true, but today it is. Also, I have to give you the regrets of Bill Nierenberg, our Director, who is in Moscow at this point. He headed for Moscow late last week — I suppose he's there by now — and will not be back for some little time.

I think that you're all well aware of the intense, long-standing interest that Scripps people have had in using diving techniques in marine science and this is basically, I guess, the reason that the meeting is being held here. In fact, it's part of the reason that Hugh Bradner is on this campus. The feeling that we have as research people is that we are well aware of the difficulties of getting our own research results over into some sphere in which they can be used in a practical, applied manner. This is always a difficult problem. I would imagine that this should be one of the principal orders of business of this meeting, to try to bridge the gap between the people who are doing research and engineering development in this field and those of you who actually go out and use equipment. I think that the Scripps people in the audience are here hoping to catch up with what's going on in the research business. Also they are hoping, perhaps, to influence the research business by some forceful display of what kinds of operational problems we have and by some forceful criticism of what kinds of things research and engineering people are producing. I hope you can help bridge this gap. I look forward to seeing the printed results, because this is always an interesting way of keeping things in proper perspective.

We'll do anything we can do to help you while you're here. I think that Jim Stewart and Hugh Bradner can take care of whatever needs arise. I stand ready to give whatever emergency help may be required. I hope you have good luck with your meeting. In your discussion, remember the old oceanographic adage that 'most whales are harponned while spouting. . .' .

Dr. Bradner: Well, at least in the early part I'm in luck; my spouts are short. Your first speaker this morning is Glen Egstrom. He's Associate Professor of Physical Education at UCLA. His research work is on varieties of environmental stress conditions, including particularly those underwater. He's a member of the UCLA group who've been developing underwater work measurement techniques and I think, as other speakers this morning, he's well known to all of you. In his case, I suspect, through his Los Angeles County Underwater Instructors Association where, I think he's president—is that right, Glen?—and on the Board of Directors of the National Association of Underwater Instructors. I think that it's appropriate to let Glen lead us off.

Let me again remind you that if you have questions, points for clarification, or possible discussions during Glen's talk, write them down on your slips of paper. Bring them up here, or give them to one of us during coffee break and we will incorporate them in the next section.

Effect of Equipment on Diving Performance
First Session

Speaker: **Dr. Glen H. Egstrom**
Department of Physical Education
University of California,
Los Angeles

Panelists: **James R. Stewart**
Diving Officer
Scripps Institution of Oceanography
La Jolla

Bev B. Morgan, President
Deepwater Development Corporation
Goleta

Lt. Cdr. Tommy Thompson
USN (Ret.)
U. S. Divers Corporation
Santa Ana

Chairman: **Dr. Hugh Bradner**
Scripps Institution of Oceanography
La Jolla

Effect of Equipment on Diving Performance

Glen H. Egstrom, Ph.D.
Department of Physical Education
University of California
Los Angeles

A Man in Armour is His Armour's Slave

The equipment related barriers to efficient, effective diver performance can be summarized if we consider a typical diver's preparation for a dive from the beach.

Initially, the diver puts on a wet suit that provides thermal protection but at the same time providing an elastic restriction to motion in the joints of the body and to the neck area. He then dons a hood which adds an additional elastic band to the throat and provides an insulation layer to interfere with hearing. Booties are added. A personal flotation vest is looped over the neck and strapped around the waist. Additional gear, such as knife, depth gauge, compass and watch are located, depending on the diver's personal choice, but usually in places where they cannot snag or foul. The tank, regulator and back pack weighing approximately 43 lbs., is strapped on the back, raising the center of gravity and providing additional standing instability. Sixteen to 18 lbs. of lead are strapped on the waist with quick release buckles located at the waist. Sturdy working gloves, which reduce tactile capability, are put on, followed by fins which permit the diver to walk backwards to his objective, and to a face plate which provides tunnel vision. To the face plate one fastens a snorkel with additional breathing resistance. However, generally the resistance in the snorkel is not as great as that provided by the regulator which will be used later.

Our diver, thus encumbered, has already accomplished a significant amount of work just getting ready to dive. In some of our observations, divers "getting ready" to dive have exhibited pulse rates in excess of

160 beats per minute, signifying moderately heavy work. Observations on Navy divers in the Sea Lab III construction teams revealed pulse rates of 170 as the diver moved into position to enter the water. This tells us that we have a partially fatigued diver, working hard, who is now ready to make an entry through the surf.

Well conditioned, experienced divers do not fined these circumstances particularly uncomfortable since they have made a successful adaptation to the specific demands involved. This adaptation, however, does not change the basic issue. Divers, while solving many of the major problems of transporting themselves beneath the sea, have created additional generations of problems, yet to be solved.

The following materials are not intended to minimize the fantastic progress which has been made in diving equipment to date but to, perhaps, lay open the need for the next generation of advancement. In the evolution of diving equipment we have passed through several stages. The early pioneers provided the basic feasibility of safe underwater life support. Later efforts extended depth and time ranges for underwater swimmers and gave us an effective underwater transport capability. More recently, a wide variety of applications of this underwater transport capability has led to a wide variety of underwater specialities, each with its own technology, but each dependent upon the diver's ability to devote his cognative and physical energies to tasks other than those of basic equipment problems. If he must be concerned about his equipment he cannot give his full attention to the task which brought him underwater. Therefore, if seems important to free the diver from as many distracting elements as possible so that he can pursue his underwater goals without hinderance.

Effect of New Equipment

The intention is that the following discussion should identify limitations and where possible speculate on needed improvements. It is not intended that this paper should cause anyone to underestimate the complexities involved in reaching adequately engineered research and development solutions to even the simplest problems.

The subject of equipment and its effect on diver performance presents a knotty problem to a variety of specialized areas of knowledge. Each piece of equipment that has been developed has been the result of an attempt to solve a specific problem related to underwater performance. Unfortunately, there has been less attention paid to the integration of these solutions into a diving system. The solution to one particular problem invariably changes the specific adaptation which the diver makes to the imposed demands of the task and the environment. For example, the solution to the problem of underwater vision has been to introduce to the diver's eyes an airspace behind a plate of glass. This very adequate solution was the result of a great deal of trial and error modification in the early stages, but face-plates have remained essentially unchanged since 1865 or thereabouts.[1] The mask and lens do, however, impose additional problems to the diver. He must systematically equalize the pressure behind the glass, keep the lens unfogged, live with a restricted visual field and appreciate the magnification and refraction errors. These requirements are indeed a small price to pay for vision, but, nevertheless, we must cope satisfactorily with this new set of conditions or we are once again in trouble. A detail such as fogging of the face plate can virtually wipe out a diver's vision if there is no satisfactory way in which to eliminate the fogging. A partially blind diver constitutes a diving hazard of serious proportion.

Such is the nature of our problem. We are faced with a continuum of "trade-offs" in order to perform effectively underwater. These trade-offs frequently violate considerations to a basic philosophy with regard to new equipment. This philosophy requires that each item of new equipment should solve more problems for the diver than it creates, or that a major problem should be solved without creating so many minor problems that they overshadow the benefits of the contribution. Implementation of this philosophy requires that a clear identification of the problem to be solved be made prior to design efforts. All too frequently we see changes in equipment which do nothing to improve the diver's lot in the interface with the basic problem of increased efficiency and effectiveness.

As man swims and works in the sea he utilizes a complex computer for solving problems and assigning work requirements to a complex series of levers. As these levers are activated, force can be exerted against a resistance over extended periods of time and effective work can be accomplished. Anything in the way of equipment which we attach ot the diver in a fashion which interferes with this basic capability results in the necessity for a specific adaptation to the new set of mechanical factors. Thus, as our technology develops equipment to meet the environmental conditions. It also alters basic mechanics of movement.

Historically, as an underwater explorer and worker, man has accepted the imposed equipment limitations with little protest since he realized that even limited work capability was better than none. A look at some of the early efforts reveals that vision received attention prior to the 13th century, utilizing tortoise shell masks of some sort. Then, just after 1900 came modern diving goggles with the inherent pressure compensation problems. It is interesting that in the year 1865 a single lens mask was made for a compressed air apparatus called the Aerophore, but that this advance had to be rediscovered for free divers about 1930, and even then it took several additional years before the realization that putting the nose inside the mask would permit equilibration and reduce squeeze. All in all, face plates have remained virtually unchanged since the 30's and few major problems have been resolved.

The face plate still provides tunnel vision, magnification, refraction, and in some cases, distortion. The sports diver adapts to these limitations and generally finds little fault with faceplates. However, the increasing demands on working divers should result in a closer look at the problem. An effort to measure the visual fields of representative existing mask configurations was conducted at UCLA. The results are summarized as follows:[2]

The normal field for two eyes extends about 60-70 upward, 100 to each side and 80 downward. The binocular field of vision has roughly the same upper and lower limits but extends about 60 to the side. A comparison of the figures shows that while upper vision is relatively free of restriction the side restriction is considerable and the lower field is severely handicapped.

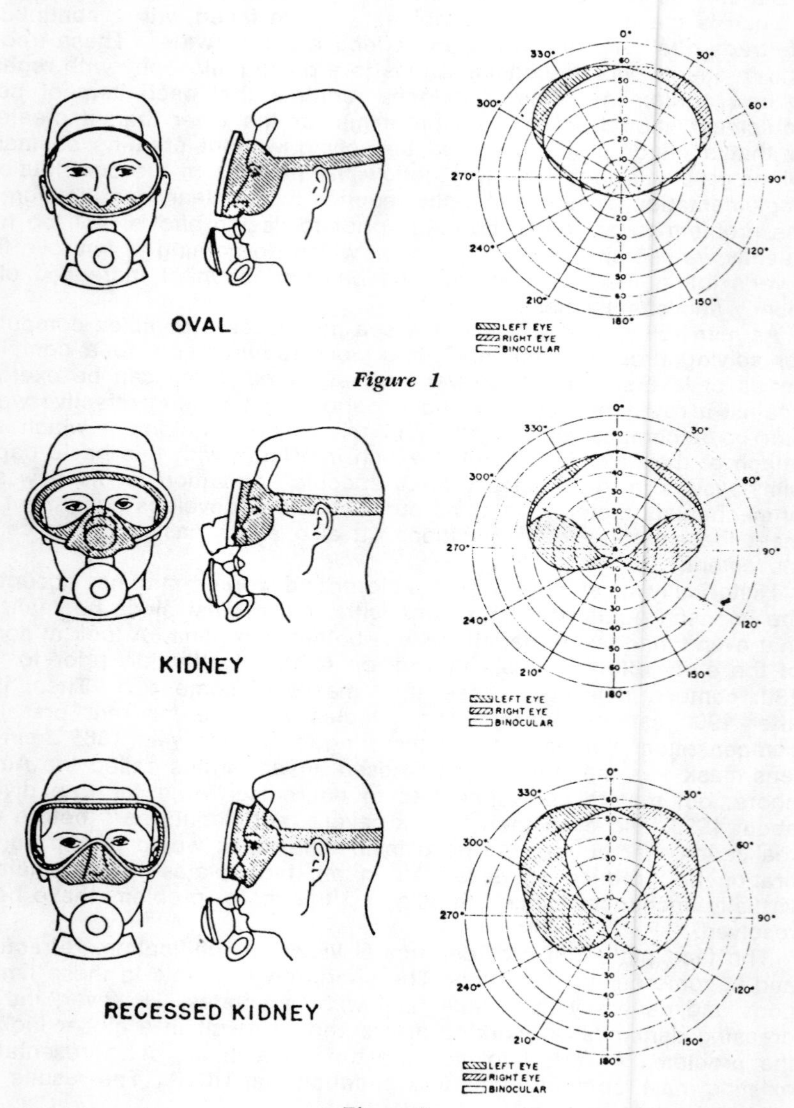

Figure 1

Figure 2

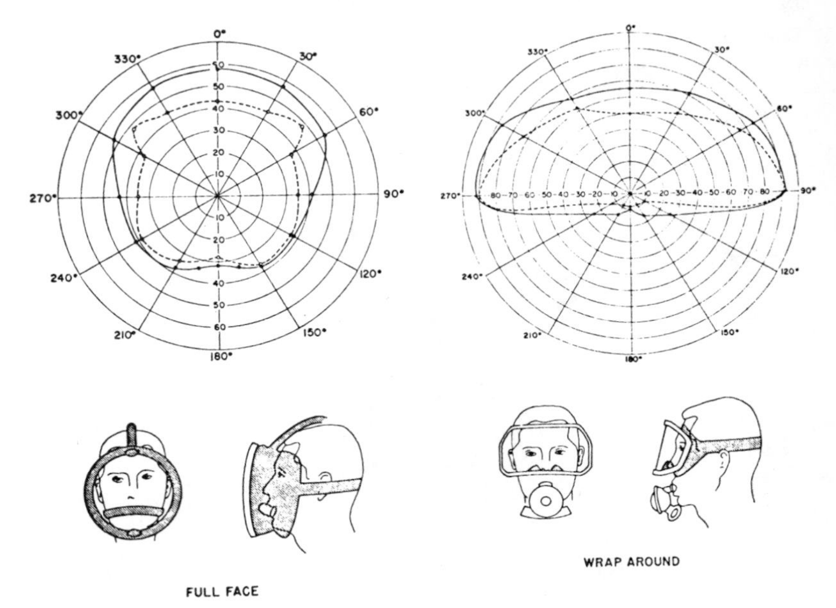

Figure 3

The full face plate, while a significant improvement, offered the disadvantage of an interdependent air supply and visual capability. The wrap-around, on the other hand, offers a wider visual field but the curvature of the glass offers distortion, and in the case of the paneled type wrap-around, the panel dividers reduce the visual field by offering "blind" areas. It appears that there is still room for an inexpensive mask configuration to afford greater fields of vision to the divers.

Divers utilizing "scuba" are also generally required to propel themselves through the water using fins of one configuration or another. These reactive forces are generated against the water throughout the kick cycle but only those force components which are resolved parallel to the long axis of the body contribute to forward motion. This component is referred to as thrust. Studies of fin performance have been conducted utilizing a specially developed underwater ergometer capable of providing reproducible work loadings for divers in a normal swimming attitude. This ergometer (figure 4) also permits a variety of physiologic measures to be made including oxygen consumption and EKG.

Our early efforts measured instantaneous static thrust generated by the swimmers. Mean thrust values were compared for leg position and thrust force during submaximal and maximal efforts using bare feet and two fin configurations. Additionally, an acceleration occurred when the legs changed direction and that the acceleration signal was reduced to near zero while the legs were crossing.

A second, more comprehensive study of fins[4] has recently been con-

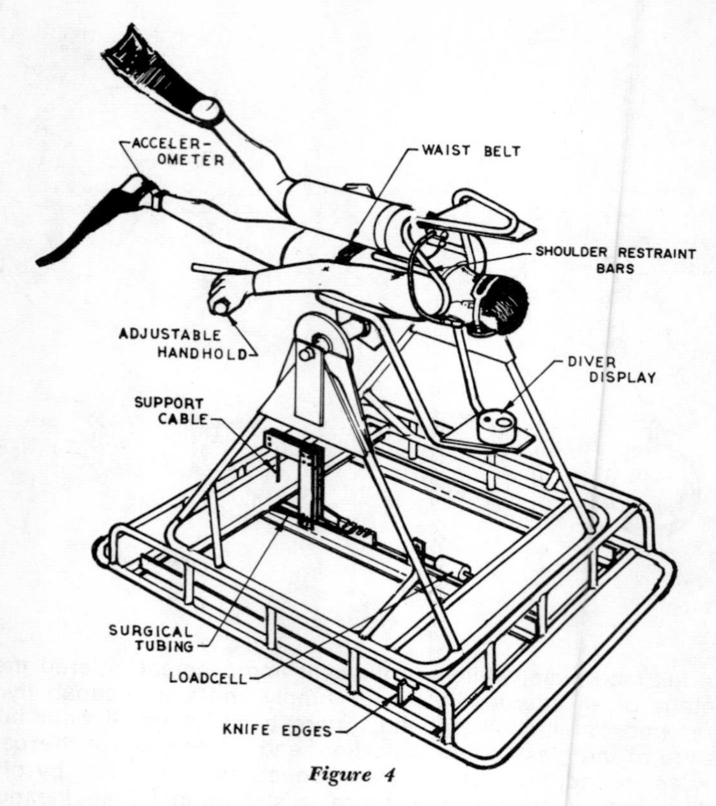

Figure 4

ducted in which nine subjects randomly worked each of nine fins under three swimming work loads — two measures were taken on each work load. Nearly 500 sets of measures were taken on thrust level, kick rate, heart rate, minute volume, CO_2 output, oxygen uptake, leg length, leg strength, body weight, age and water temperature. This data was then programmed for computer analysis and reviewed. A complete report is forthcoming but I should like to present a few preliminary observations at this time.

The first observation is that there is a remarkable lack of consistency in answer to the question "which fin is best?". Individuals appear to exhibit some preferences but if the three fins which scored highest for each individual were plotted, every fin in the study would end up as "one of the top three" for at least one of the subjects. There did appear to be a tendency in favor of some of the more flexible fins for the subjects who were less experienced and in lower states of condition, but to identify any fin as "obviously superior" would be impossible. However, the reader should recognize that only top of the line fins in the extra large sizes were used in the study, and that four of the styles were of the adjustable heel strap type.

It also appears that the divers with the longer legs are able to use the fins at a lower energy cost than the divers with the shorter legs. It is possible that fins should be fitted to individuals with the same care that shoes are fitted. It is hoped that criteria for this type of evaluation will be forthcoming.

Snorkel tubes have been considered as basic diving equipment since the beginnings of the sport. These tubes provide the diver with the ability to work along on the surface of the water with his face submerged in order to view the underwater scene. At low work loads these tubes are adequate and little difficulty is encountered. However, let the diver begin to work hard and the snorkel becomes a limiting factor.

The volume of air which one moves during exercise will vary almost directly with work load during aerobic metabolism. However, during hyperventilation, an exponential increase takes place and excessive minute volumes occur. An adequate snorkel should permit the movement of all of the air necessary for heavy work loads and even hyperventilation, since the rejection of the snorkel is the only other alternative. This alternative is generally considered to be an unsafe practice. Any breathing apparatus should be able to deliver maximal amounts of air at minimal resistance levels for human requirements. Some of these requirements are listed below:

Minute Volume 75 lpm - peak flow 250
Minute Volume 100 lpm - peak flow 325
Minute Volume 120 lmp - peak flow 390

These are volumes and peak flows found in the range of moderately heavy to severe physical exertion and can be achieved by most reasonably fit individuals.

Airway resistances and flow capabilities of 14 snorkel configurations have been studied, and it was concluded that only three configurations were capable of meeting the requirements for even the moderately heavy work loads. These configurations had several common features. Their design include a larger diameter airway with a minimum of curvature, and they were consistently shorter than the less acceptable tubes. It should be remembered that individual variations in respiratory work capability are such that not all individuals require extreme large diameter tubes. However, it is a rare individual who cannot move at least 75 lpm of air during exercise.

Several factors appear important:

(1) The reduction of turbulent flow of air through the tube by one-half will reduce the amount of respiratory force necessary to move the air by a factor of four. Thus bends, restrictions, corregations and small diameter tubes are all to be avoided as much as possible.

(2) Instrumental dead space should be reduced. The problem can be better appreciated if we recognize that breathing against a resistance brings about a decrease in pulmonary ventilation and results in an increased carbon dioxide loading as well as a reduction in available oxygen. Breathing through a snorkel adds dead space to the

respiratory system. Alveolar ventilation per minute is equal to the respiratory rate times the amount of new air that enter the alveoli with each breath. An increase in the dead space volume will decrease the alveolar ventilation. If the rate and depth of respiration are kept constant under conditions of work and rest, the net alveolar ventilation preceded by each breath is reduced in proportion to the dead space added. Normally, the body tries to compensate for this added dead space by increasing ventilation. Increasing the depth of breathing gives the most effective compensation. If rate alone is increased, much of the ventilation is wasted on dead space and oxygen consumption of respiratory muscles increases disproportionately. Increased ventilation cannot compensate completely for considerable amount of dead space; it must draw on the individual's respiratory reserve, thus decreasing his capacity for physical exertion.[6]

(3) The range of sizing in snorkel tubes should follow the requirements for minute volume, peak flow rates and low levels of resistance necessary to permit individuals to perform heavy work.

Thermal protection has been provided primarily by rubber suits. Their development has followed an interesting course. An article[7] in the Sunday news describes the adventures of one "Capt." Paul Boyton who utilized a rubber suit constructed by C. S. Merriman during the year 1874. A look at this suit demonstrates a remarkable similarity to today's recent advances in hot water heated suits. He used the suit to float down most of the major waterways of the world, and in 1875 paddled across the English Channel in a little under 24 hours. He made regular trips of 400 to 500 miles, stopping on the way to enjoy the good life.

The wet suit of today if fitted with care is generally quite comfortable. However, it does provide an elastic case which limits range of motion in most joints of the body. Extra energy is required to move the joints, particularly in the case of utilization of heavier or less elastic materials. In many cases where a tight fit has been achieved the work of respiration is elevated. Constriction around the neck by the collar may also be contributing to a carotid sinus squeeze of significant proportions.

However, this suit which changes its bouyancy capability as a function of depth, does provide enough thermal protection to permit extended dives in colder water. The addition of a hood is necessary and usually fits under the suit collar providing a double thickness of elastic around the throat. However, the hood is necessary due to the very high rate of heat loss which can occur from the head. Edwards and Buton[8] concluded that the insulation of the head did not change with environmental temperature, was independent of the thermal state of the body and that heat loss from the head alone in extreme cold may account for up to half the total resting heat production of the individual. Hoods which are built into vests or which are built onto the diving suit offer some advanages but fit becomes critical.

Bootees may be of two basic types, soft neoprene like the wet suits, or a tougher material (rock socks). The rock sock provides adequate protection against rocks and gravel while walking but offers little thermal protection. The neoprene booty offers much better thermal protection but wears out rapidly and tears easily. Recent efforts at incorporating a hard sole to a neoprene booty are encouraging but is still under development.

The personal flotation vest, which was adapted from an early emergency flotation vest, has proven to be expensive and generally unsatisfactory for use by active divers. It seems obvious that some type of individual buoyancy control is advantageous but the problems associated with most vests now in use have led to a widespread dissatisfaction. Again, progress is being made in developing non-corrosive parts, shorter vests which do not overlap the weight belt, quick release, flotation chambers which expand away from the body strap, etc. But no vest currently on the market provides integrated, reliable buoyancy control which is free from obvious disadvantages in the interface with other components of diving gear. Several factors are involved here. It would seem reasonable that the flotation vest should provide buoyancy control without significant interference with the diver's work capability. Most present vests ride up under the diver's chin when they are partially inflated and further reduce the diver's ability to work effectively. This disadvantage when added to the problems with valves, inflators, easily torn materials, etc., leads to speculation that buoyancy control might better be integrated into the system in some yet untried, but hopefully more satisfactory way.

Scuba regulators as we know them have their beginnings about 1865 when two Frenchmen, Rouquayrol and Denayrouse, developed a diving apparatus which utilized the demand concept successfully in a full diving suit. This major innovation set the stage for a series of improvements and the development of both closed circuit and open circuit Scuba. The early 1900's saw much effort applied to submarine escape devices in which the previously discovered principles were applied to much smaller packages. By 1926 the Fernez-LePrieur self contained diving apparatus had become a reality. However, refinements over a 10 year period continued to use free flow delivery of air to the diver, and larger compressed gas tanks at higher pressures were required to increase bottom time.

The major breakthrough was provided when Jacques Cousteau and Emile Gagnan installed a demand valve into a compressed gas supply on the order to LePrieur's. This system was refined during WW II and reached the commercial market in small quantities about 1947 under the name "Aqua-Lung". During the next 20 years we have witnessed an explosive growth in the number of diver's and there is now a well-defined, competitive diving equipment industry. This industry provides a variety of equipment designed to appeal to the tastes of the diving public. It is interesting to note that the basic equipment configurations have changed very little since their invention and differ very little at the functional level.

Let us consider the problem which regulators must overcome to be effective. The regulator must deliver ambient pressure gas to the diver in sufficient quantity to permit a full range of physical work without deleterious effects on the diver's well being.

Respiration Resistance (inches of water)
Single Hose Regulators

	Peak Flow LPM	25	50	75	100	125	150	175	200	225	250
REGULATOR #1 Typical Single Exhaust (small)	Inhalation	2.1	2.1	2.1	2.1	2.1	2.0	2.0	1.8	1.7	1.6
	Exhalation	1.3	1.9	2.2	2.7	3.4	4.0	4.6	5.2		
REGULATOR #2 Large Exhaust	Inhalation	2.2	2.2	2.2	2.2	2.2	2.2	2.2	2.1	2.1	2.0
	Inhalation*	4.1	4.3	4.4	4.5	4.6	4.6	4.7	4.6	4.6	4.6
	Exhalation	.6	.8	1.0	1.2	1.6	1.8	2.1	2.4		
REGULATOR #3 Large Exhaust	Inhalation	2.1	2.1	2.1	2.2	2.3	2.5	2.6	2.8	2.9	3.1
	Exhalation	1.8	1.8	1.9	2.1	2.3	2.7	3.0	3.3		
REGULATOR #4 Large Exhaust	Inhalation	2.2	2.3	2.4	2.4	2.4	2.3	2.3	2.2	2.1	2.0
	Exhalation	.4	.7	19	1.3	1.9	2.5	3.1	3.5		
REGULATOR #5 Dual Exhaust (small)	Inhalation	1.5	1.4	1.3	1.3	1.2	1.1	1.0	.8	.6	.4
	Exhalation	.6	.9	1.2	1.5	1.9	2.2	2.6	2.9		

*A resistance modifier installed * denotes full restricted position on inhalation. "I" full open.

Early development of regulators enabled man to dive under the water and return alive. Regulators were then modified to permit underwater swimming at light work loads, and have recently evolved into configurations which will permit moderate to heavy underwater work. These recent regulators have been designed with both inhalation and exhalation effort reduced significantly from the earlier models. A recent survey of the regulators from four of the leading manufacturers revealed that the models with larger exhaust capabilities and advanced first stages have performance capabilities as shown in Table 1.

These data are derived from peak flow rates and do not accurately reflect the values which are found under actual underwater work conditions. A device to perform these measurements is presently under development and should be in use soon.

Measurements indicate that the better regulators, when well tuned, are providing negative pressure breathing in the range of 2½ inches of water pressure resistance. Ceretelli, et al.,[10] have concluded that the addition of resistance load to the respiratory apparatus reduces the minute volume at any level of exercise with reduction in ventilation being directly related to increase in resistance. In addition there is a diuresis effect which results from negative pressure breathing that appears to add significantly to other factors such as cold, immersion and exercise in the overall water balance upsets. Beckman[11] has reported that the onset of diuresis begins within a half hour of the time of immersion and continues for periods up to 24 hours. This water diuresis progresses with continuous output of low specific gravity urine even though constant dehydration amounting to 6 pounds of water in 12 hours occurred. This diuresis effect was amplified in a number of other immersion studies.[12,13,14,15] However, Graveline and Jackson,[16] point out that immersion alone can produce diuresis even in adjusted positive pressure breathing. It also appears that a number of respiratory changes should be expected, and although they do not appear to be serious limiting factors, they should be considered.

Significant decreases in vital capacity and expiratory reserve volume have been identified and have led to observations that 6-11 mmhg positive pressure is necessary to achieve full lung compartmentalization. Effects of negative pressure breathing in shallow water studies indicate that relatively small amounts (6″-8″ water) of resistance results in up to 20 percent decrease in tidal volume, 64 percent decrease in mean expiratory volume, 32 percent decrease in mean inspiratory volume and a 3 percent decrease in vital capacity. In addition, there appears to be a prolonged diuresis that has continued for days.

A number of factors contribute to the water losses and indicate that efforts should be made to develop equipment which will encourage a more normal water balance. This seems important in light of the work of Cockett which points out the advantages of adequate fluids in bends treatment.

The present generation of regulators also poses problems for communication which effectively blocks one of our most important behavioral modifying capabilities. Hollien has demonstrated that diver intelligibility levels with existing communication equipment are generally unsatisfactory in that a test of 11 systems revealed a high score of only 52.3 percent intelligibility. Much of the problem appears to reside in the diver's use of the equipment rather than in the equipment itself. The various mouth cup devices which have been employed in the more successful systems are still somewhat restrictive and cumbersome with complicated attachment systems and switches. These systems operate with some success in trained talker-listener relationships. However, what is still needed is an effective, short range communicator that will enable divers to identify problems, receive information and give directions routinely at a level that is equivalent to that found in other environments where communication provides for safer behavior.

REFERENCES

[1] Larson, Howard E., *A History of Self-Contained Diving and Underwater Swimming,* National Academy of Sciences, Committee on Undersea Warfare, Publication # 469, 1959.
[2] Weltman, G., Christianson, R. A., & Egstrom, G., "Visual Fields of Scuba Divers", *Human Factors,* October, 1965.
[3] Christianson, R. A., Weltman, G., & Egstrom, G., "Thrust Forces in Underwater Swimming". *Human Factors,* December, 1965.
[4] Egstrom, G., & Weltman, G., "Fin Swimming and Metabolic Cost", unpublished data, 1970.
[5] Weltman, G., Egstrom, G., and Christianson, R. A., "A System for Underwater Ergometry", AIAA Paper #66-173.
[6] Bureau of Medicine & Surgery, *Submarine Medical Practice,* Bureau of Naval Personnel, U. S. Government Printing Office, Washington, D. C., 1956.
[7] Ferris, John, "Forgotten First", *Sunday News,* November 3, 10, 17, 1968.
[8] Edwards, M. & Burton, A., "Correlation of Heat Output and Blood Flow in the Finger, Especially in Cold Induced Vasodilation", *Journal of Applied Physiology,* 15:2, 1960.
[9] Dugan, James, *Man Under the Sea,* Collier Books, New York, 1965.
[10] Cerritelli, P. et. al., "Effect of Increased Airway Resistance on Ventilation and Gas Exchange during Exercise", *Journal of Applied Physiology,* 27:5, 1969.
[11] Beckman, E. et. al., "Physiologic Changes Observed in Human Subjects During Zero G Simulation by Immersion in Water up to Neck Level", *Aerospace Medicine,* November, 1961.
[12] Hunt, N. C. III, "Positive Pressure Breathing During Water Immersion," *Aerospace Medicine,* July, 1967.
[13] Hood, W. B. et. al., "Circulatory Effects of Water Immersion upon Human Subjects", *Aerospace Medicine,* June, 1968.
[14] Vogt, F. & Jackson, O., "Study of Effect of Water Immersion on Healthy Male Subjects: Plasma Volume and Fluid-Electrolyte Changed", *Aerospace Medicine,* May, 1965.
[15] Campbell, L. et. al., "Cardiovascular Responses to Partial and Total Immersion in Man", *Journal of Physiology,* 202:, 1969.
[16] Graveline, D. & Jackson, M., "Diuresis Associated with Prolonged Water Immersion" *Journal of Applied Physiology,* 17:3, 1962.
[17] Cockett, A. & Nakamura, R., "A New Concept in the Treatment of Decompression Sickness (Dysbarism)", *Lancet,* May 16, 1964.
[18] Hollien, H. et. al., "Underwater Speech Communication", Communciation Sciences Laboratory Report #11, Gainesville, Florida, December 15, 1966.

REACTION 1
Opening Session

James R. Stewart
Diving Officer
Scripps Institution of Oceanography

In Dr. Egstrom's presentation he pretty well defines the limits of our existing equipment. Assuming an individual is competent and comfortable in the water, has been properly trained in the use of his equipment, and understands the physical environment in which he will be working, many of the equipment problems referred to seem relatively unimportant in our experience.

In scientific diving, our most usual foe is cold. In scientific and technical fields the individual often remains fairly inactive — observing, recording data, or reading or repairing instruments. The first region affected is usually the hands, limiting the diver's tactile sense. Using gloves available today makes the sense useless to touch to begin with. Individuals who dive without hoods often find themselves impaired by severe headaches. Heat loss from the head area is considerable but in addition water entering the suit at the neck lowers the overall body temperature. A number of permutations of suit thicknesses, configurations, and materials have been tried. It is generally agreed the "farmer-John" style pants, shirt with attached hood and no zippers, bootees of suit material, and rubber gloves give maximum warmth. This is desirable only in the coldest areas in which man works, as one pays a large price in ease of movement and breathing. Coupled with cold is a change of bouyancy with depth as a function of suit compression. When working on vertical faces of sub-marine canyons, or on buoys in open water, there is no bottom to step on or to provide support. When the diver is deep enough that his suit is considerably compressed, the negative bouyancy, or heaviness, often becomes an acute problem. Thus, at present there is a real need for a simple reliable personal bouyancy control device which will allow the diver to trim himself neutral at any depth or to off-set the weight of an object to be transported from one point to another. Current designs of life vests because of their unreliable detonation mechanisms are not reliable. In an emergency dropping the weight belt is the safer answer.

One situation in which one might find present regulators limiting his effectiveness is doing strenuous work in open water as described earlier. An example of such work is changing transducers on ships, removing bolts and nuts with a breaker bar or other simple man-powered wrenches in places which cannot be reached by a larger air or hydraulic tool. Actually, however, one finds he can adapt himself to the equipment, rather than being defeated by its limitations. Controlled rhythmic breathing, consciously utilized prevents over-breathing the unit and avoids a CO_2 build-up.

Man is really an ingenious and adaptable animal. Although he faces constraints imposed by the equipment of today, he gets much done. Basically, improvement is needed on the generalized problems of vision, communication, cold and propelling a rectangular chunk through a dense medium. Using the criteria of dollar value versus usefulness, one currently finds off-the-shelf equipment adequate to conduct his operations. By usefulness, I explicitly mean reliability, efficiency, and ease of achieving high standards of maintenance. The one gap in our capabilities to more easily complete our underwater tasks is a communication system. This will be discussed later in the session.

REACTION 2
Opening Session

Future SCUBA Equipment Design

Bev B. Morgan, President
Deepwater Development Corporation

We divers concurrently live in two worlds. One is the real world. The real world in diving is just that: what actually occurs and what is actually needed to overcome the burdens. The assumed world in diving is what each diver assumes to be "real". There are as many assumed worlds in diving as there are divers. It is necessary, therefore, to conduct research such as Dr. Egstrom is doing to find what is actually happening to divers and what is needed to improve the diver's lot. It is equally important for the results of such work to be applied to influence equipment design. Each of us should be devoted to bringing forth the real world of diving.

I suspect that Dr. Egstrom's statement, "Well conditioned, experienced divers do not find these circumstances particularly uncomfortable since they have made a successful adaptation to the specific demands involved," could use elaboration. Many divers cover up problems to create the assumption to observers that they are "good" divers. If an exposure suit designer is an observer, his assumed world of diving is strongly influenced by the diver who is cold, but reports that he is "warm as toast" to continue his "good diver" pattern. As a matter of fact, the diver may have even convinced himself that the cold "isn't that bad". Needless to say, I am sure we all have heard a tale or two by divers that are obviously false, yet the diver himself is convinced it is true. The exposure suit designer that employs instruments to gather data will be more successful.

Without dwelling further on the interrelation of physiology, behavior, equipment, and methods, let us look at SCUBA diving equipment from a designer's viewpoint.

SCUBA diving encompasses the sport, professional, military, and research diving. The following lists the important aspects of going underwater that determines the design of equipment.

Diver Equipment

1. RESPIRATION: The Self Contained Underwater Breathing Apparatus, (SCUBA) is the single piece of equipment that diver *must have* for prolonged periods underwater. He cannot survive without it.
2. BOUYANCY CONTROL: *Must* be present.
3. SIGHT: The diver *should have* a method of seeing underwater. Although inconvenient, he can not survive without it.
4. WARMTH: Another *should have.*
5. VOICE COMMUNICATIONS: A should have that ranks fifth in importance for diver performance, yet little has been done to bring this important necessity within the reach of most divers.
6. PROPULSION: *Should have* for specific applications.
7. INSTRUMENTS: Time, Depth, etc., *should be* available.
8. TOOLS: No specific jobs, tools *should be* available.

SUPPORT EQUIPMENT AND CONDITIONS

1. Living facilities.
2. Equipment facilities.
3. Supplies.
4. Transportation facilities to dive site.
5. Physical fitness.
6. Proper training in diving safety including emergency procedures.
7. Procedure plans for underwater excursions.

Assuming the reader is knowledgeable in SCUBA equipment that is currently available, I offer only the following comment: There has not been a major improvement in design in 10 years.

The future of diving equipment will be controlled by the originality of the designer, the consumer, demand, and the consumer's willingness to pay for improvements.

My design work has been concentrated on the first five items listed under "Diver Equipment" above. The following is my opinion on what to expect in the next five years.

1. RESPIRATION: Better regulators for open circuit SCUBA divers will be available. Inhalation resistance will be less than one inch of water pressure. Exhalation resistance may be improved, but only slightly if at all. Water spraying on inhalation, a common occurrence in today's regulators, will be eliminated.

   Better semi and closed circuit breathing apparatus will be available for special applications such as deep diving. Inhalation and exhalation efforts will be eliminated. The apparatus will supply intake and exhaust breathing gasses at over and under pressures. If the diver passes out, the apparatus will automatically take over the breathing cycle and signal for assistance.
2. BOUYANCY CONTROL: Although an important factor in diving, this is tied closely with the exposure suit and has not presented a serious problem in the past. A radical departure from current methods of insulation will eliminate the necessity of wearing weights for neutralizing suit bouyancy.

3. SIGHT: Face masks for divers will change in the next five years. Although methods of extending the diver's field of vision exist even today, these will not be accepted. This will be due to the resulting change in depth perception and vision disorientations that accompany any changes in the flat lens system now in use. Rather, the mask will be called upon to do functions in addition to providing vision. A workable, convenient system of providing a space for voice communication and providing a mounting platform for electronics packages will change the appearance of today's masks.

   Some deep divers will be equipped with a complete helmet which will provide a superior convenience over today's masks, yet provide dry atmosphere for the ears to improve communication.
4. WARMTH: Divers will be well underway to a new material in suits. Foam neoprene will be replaced with a non-gas filled material that will not change bouyancy and will be far less bouyant. Entrapment of body heat will be improved and methods of adding heat will be available. Current wet suits made of foamed neoprene will still be around but the knowledgeable diver will be shifting to a new material.
5. VOICE COMMUNICATIONS: The largest change in diving will be the availability of a system of voice communications within the price range of the average sport diver. Well over 50 percent of all sports divers will be talking to each other underwater within five years.

REACTION 3
Opening Session

Effect of Equipment on Diving Performance

Lt. CDR. Tommy Thompson (Ret.)
Public Relations Director
U. S. Divers Association

In general, I agree with Dr. Egstrom's remarks regarding the burden put on the human being sent under the water to do productive work. However, one must look at some other things involved, i.e., cost, and the many years involved, and how many people actually know or have any interest in the problems.

Captain Cousteau tells the story of the beginning of Aqua-Lung diving in America. In 1948 a total of 12 units were sent from France to Los Angeles for sale in this country. Then, in 1949, when Cousteau inquired about the number of units that could be sold in this country during the year, he was informed that he could have 12 more units shipped from France, but that they would not sell because the U. S.

market was already saturated. That, gentlemen, was only 21 years ago.

Face masks were first made in 1865, according to Dr. Egstrom. Less than a quarter of a century ago the Aqua-lung market was thought to be saturated with only 12 units.

Dick Anderson stated that "In 1948 I was the second most powerful man in the diving equipment business in the United States." There were only two men in the equipment business at that time. We are a young and growing industry with growing pains. No one is even asking why a fin, mask or snorkel is this shape. Only within the last three years has anyone even thought about or mentioned air flow or resistance.

Finances — how much the ultimate in equipment will cost — must be a major consideration. This small exhaust valve required in every single hose regulator is molded by us to require a minimum opening effort. But it must have sufficient strength so that it will not tear when it is hot and being removed by hand from the mold.

It must be thick enough so it will not take a permanent set or work when it is sitting on the dive shop shelf. A variation of .001th of an inch will make this exhaust valve acceptable or rejectable.

Diving is a small industry. People are feeling their way as they go. Designers, engineers, technicians are being trained as they go along. Lots of progress has been made . . . lost more is needed.

The two most pressing needs in the diving profession at the present time are thermal protection and communication. There is no practical way to keep a diver warm at 200 feet when the surrounding water is only 50° F. There is no way to communicate with a diver only 200 feet away when helium is used as a breathing gas. Yet loud and clear voices can be heard from the moon, a quarter of a million miles away.

The diving profession needs people such as Dr. Egstrom to bring the problems to the attention of all of us. Perhaps what we need most is explained on page 527 in the book "Deep Diving and Submarine Operations" by Robert H. Davis. This is called "submarine twins" where a professional diver takes a professional engineer down with him in a diving dress with only three sleeves for the two of them. This was to insure that the fellow who might solve some of our problems was made fully aware of those problems.

DISCUSSION
Opening Session

Audience question: Do not suppliers of diving equipment seem more interested in salability of the product than the proper design? What is your suggestion or solution?

Dr. Egstrom: What is my solution? I don't have a solution, but I have some biases. One of these is related to the fact that one of our instructors made a comment sometime ago that he was wondering how

long it was going to take the equipment manufacturers to reach the point where they weren't going to be using the public, the diving public, to test their equipment. This is the point that I would make. It seems to me that the industry and the sport has grown to the point where in the development of equipment we should expect, not only quality control inspections, but laboratory tests of the equipment to determine what the functional capabilities of that gear are. These inhouse laboratory tests would then be followed by field tests across the population sample that would be using equipment in the way it is going to be used by the sport divers or work divers. After these evaluation procedures are completed, a re-evaluation, a relook at the design would take place, last-minute modifications made, and then the equipment would be put into production. I realize that that's an unpopular viewpoint from the standpoint of business because it costs money. I think if we look at comparable kinds of manufacturing activities in other areas that we'll see that ultimately we'll have to have a systematic way of determining limitations of the equipment. We have to know whether that equipment is really going to do the job or not.

Audience question: How soon can we expect to have engineers who really understand the problems of diving?

Dr. Egstrom: You have a point there. We're long overdue for the development of engineers who really understand the problems of diving. Some of this gear that goes across Tommy Thompson's desk that we take out and dive, really, they're horrors. The reason that the equipment is so bad — the technical engineering aspects are not so bad — but it is often designed by people who really don't understand diving. One communications gear I recall had about 13 to 14 different straps and things around it. By the time you got all of this garbage on, you were lucky to be able to stay alive. They put bubble diffusers on the outside of the regulator so that the exhalation resistance went up into the range of something like 13 to 14 inches of water. It had a diaphragm inhalation valve that, I think, was made out of someone's old shoe soles because Tommy was getting to the point where he was literally turning blue, just trying to make the darn machine work. Someone had spent several thousand dollars on it.

Audience question: Do you have anything new on regulators?

Dr. Egstrom: I'd like to point out one little thing that has come to our attention, at least in recent times. The metal plate on the diaphragm on a single-hose regulator and the metal yoke that rides on that plate to manipulate the valve is the site of one of the kinds of resistance problems that is involved in the regulator. A young fellow who does our maintenance began to look at this. He found that one of the ways he could make the regulator breathe easier after it's been used for a while was to polish off the corrosion on most metal-to-metal surfaces. Now, if this was plastic, it would seem to me that we might not have that particular kind of problem. Thank you.

Dr. Bradner: I think that both Tommy and Bev would like to expand and argue on the same subject quite extensively. However, perhaps I should solicit — beginning now — some questions from the audience.

If you would like to be identified in the record, please state your name. I'll repeat the question. Yes, Bev.

Mr. Morgan: Should we respond to some of these initially?

Dr. Bradner: I would leave this up to the audience. My suspicion is that by now they might like to divert into questions that they've been holding. Let me try it. I'll solicit questions from here. Yes?

Dr. Bradner: The question is, at what point do the panelists consider a recompression chamber to be a necessary part of diving equipment?

Lt. Cdr. Thompson: Any time. My response is any time you're diving deeper than 33 feet, if you're going to be there long enough. It's common sense. I would say anytime that you're diving deeper than a 100 feet, you not only should have a recompression chamber available, but you should have people who are expert in the treatment of the decompression sickness. If you're a sport diver going out to get five abalone, no; but I mean if you're working to the depths, it would be my response to it.

Mr. Stewart: I think it's a function of depth and time. I think you pretty well know your diving areas. You know what you're going to do. You at least should know where the chambers are and have an emergency procedure set up to handle anything that does occur, whether you personally have one or not.

Mr. Morgan: In the commercial industry, any work from 100 feet or deeper, you must have a tube-locked chamber on the dive site. I would say that the amateur diver shouldn't go into decompression times at any time unless he is under supervision and has the chamber available. Let's put it this way, a working diver or professional diver has to undergo certain financial limitations and has to take certain risks in order to earn his money because of competition. But someone doing it for sport shouldn't get involved. He should stay on free time and he's safe.

Dr. Egstrom: Right now at the national level there are a number of agencies investigating the responsibility for providing the kind of thing Commander Hoke has mentioned. There is reason to believe that we're going to see some instructions coming out that may even require diving charter boats to have chamber capability. Emergency chamber facilities will be spotted at places where there are heavy diving incidences. We've been noticing an alarming increase in the number of accidents which result in death or accidents that result in near misses which could be helped if chamber facilities were available immediately. If we continue to have the number of accidents off diving boats that we are seeing, then the kind of thing that is . . . Tom, is it your company that gave the chamber to Avalon?

Lt. Cdr. Thompson: Avalon, hospital in Avalon.

Dr. Egstrom: . . . where they've had to put at least a pressurized stretcher capability spotted in key locations for use. I think that we are, in fact, going to see a great deal more of this in the future.

Dr. Bradner: I think we've hit a unique first question and reply in that each of the panelists had something extremely significant that needed to be said. However, your question.

Audience question: The loss of body electrolytes, should fluids be prescribed to replace this?

Dr. Egstrom: This afternoon Commander Hoke is going to spend a good deal of time on this particular problem in his presentation. If you don't mind I'd like to defer the question until this afternoon. It would be more appropriate then.

Audience question: What are the prospects for a plastic compressed air tank and, second, the expectation for federal regulation of diving similar to FAA?

Lt. Cdr. Thompson: I'll take the one on the tank. There are many fiber-wound tanks. Many of them are being used in pressures greater than what we ever experience in diving breathing gases. However, many things that the tank manufacturers have not looked at, one in particular that I've had experience with. We do not know the saturation of fiber-wound tanks when they're completely submerged in salt water for a period of time. This was brought home a few years ago when an air compressor company by the name of Joy made high pressure air compressors. They used the fiber-wound volume tank receiver. Well, even picking up the moisture out of the atmosphere (I was acquainted with it in the San Pedro area) these fiber-wound tanks after a certain length of time would become porous and would leak air. The same thing happens in diving tanks. After they're exposel in salt water for a period of time and we don't know exactly when, it depends on how they are made. You follow the diver along and he looks like a sieve. He's bubbling all along the back. It's safe enough as long as it's doing that. But if it carries away, it is not compatible with good health. We just haven't had the experience. We don't know. I looked at some fiber glass tanks, oh, less than a month ago and, of course, this was after they are acceptable to the public. When I know they're safe enough for me to use, then we must prove over a series of tests and years of experience to the Department of Transportation, of course, before they will accept them to transport them on a public highway.

Dr. Bradner: Glen, would you like to give a brief report of your views on the prospects for FAA-type of regulation on that?

Dr. Egstrom: Yes. I've been involved in two panels just recently where this problem was discussed. It is apparent, from the information from some of the legislators and people involved in implementing some of the safety requirements that we face, that the feeling is that education is still the better way to go. Because of the increased incidence of accidents and because of the lack of adequate information on accidents, two things appear to be in the offing. One, the development of an accident reporting system, an evaluation system, handled by some agency. Two, the development of regulations in areas that are going to be enforceable.

We have within the Council for National Cooperation on Aquatics a series of committees. One of these committees, the Z-86 committee, is charged with the responsibility of establishing standards with the American Standards Institute for diving qualifications, for instructor qualfication, for equipment standardization, and this sort of thing. When this is completed, there are ilkely to be regulations that will cover such things as air, probably equipment and quite possibly in the long run, certification. I doubt that we're going to see this sort of thing, licensing, that the FAA is involved in if we can demonstrate that our educational capability is going to handle the problem. But, if we keep on having accidents at the rate that they've been accumulating during the last couple of years in the sports industry, then I think that we can start to see local regulation and finally state control.

Mr. Morgan: I might be kind of a radical on this, but I think all we need is a Nader's Raiders deal in the diving industry because the real power of straightening this whole darn thing out is in getting after the manufacturers. The only way to do it is through the consumers. And, you can't get the consumers and have them to operate in concert with the thing unless you have some way of reaching them with the pros and cons of the thing. Really, in all fairness, I'm not trying to pick on Tommy here. Be fair to the companies. Look at Tommy's problem from his viewpoint. He comes up with pieces. . . .

Lt. Cdr. Thompson: Let me state my own problems.

Sure, we've got problems. I agree with Glen and Bev. If we don't do something — and this is what I preach all the time — if we ourselves who know the problems that we're faced with and know the solution, don't do something about it, then someone is going to do it for us. We will have to live with it. I presented a paper one time and told people that I did not want my diving equipment, or how I'm going to be trained, or where I'm going to dive, or when, regulated from Sacramento, from Tallahassee, from Topeka or any other place. But, if we don't do it ourselves, someone else is and that is a problem! We have to be careful because everyone likes to see their name in print. As the Governor of Florida told me one time, "We're not looking for legislation, but let's face it. We've got a lot of new Senators and Representatives; they've got to sponsor a bill of some kind, you know, and this is a good one."

Audience question: Is there a communication problem?

Mr. Stewart: You might be interested in something we had happen here this week where apparently we had an embolism, pneumothorax, or any combination of these events take place here in our canyon. A person came up from 100 feet and, if you can imagine a man running out of air at 130 feet, buddy-breathing to the hundred-foot level, and somehow losing the fellow with the air. I really can't understand that. The guy with the air came up first and then the second guy, who was out of air, bubbling and frothing and doing all the good things. They got him in to the beach and they took him to the Scripps Hospital. Now the police apparently had no understanding of the problems. They took him to the Scripps Hospital rather than trying to reach a recompression chamber. So a little education has to be cranked in here some place.

Audience question: The panelists considered the use of notice to mariners as a way of disseminating information on such things as the availability of recompression chambers. Am I narrowing it too much?

Dr. Bradner: And to alert people for the particulars concerning an accident. Does anybody feel that calls for a remark?

Dr. Egstrom: Yes. There is an office in the Coast Guard in Washington manned by Captain Swint studying underwater problems. Presently they are reviewing whether or not they should take the leadership in the very thing that you're talking about and use that particular chain for getting information. There may be some complications here because the Coast Guard is only in the chain that exists at the present time insofar as accidents which occur on vessels or off the coast. They don't get involved in accidents which come in over the beach.

Now, there is a possibility, and this is something that a group has been working on. In Los Angeles County we have what we think is an adequate, implementable system for handling diving accident statistics. What we're trying to do now is to develop enough interest so that we can spread this across the country, because in the cases of fatalities you need the cooperation of the law enforcement agencies and the coroner's office. In the cases of near-misses, we have to have a network where the individual who has the problem will sit down and objectively fill out the accident report form without giving in to the temptation to become the hero of the piece. It seems that usually when a person survives a near-miss in diving, he reports that, "I survived because I'm such a superpowerful diver who didn't lose his self control: I really kept my cool." They rarely go back and recognize that they really brought the problem on themselves at the beginning by unsafe practice. They become a hero and give inaccurate information. What we have been finding, incidentally, just for your information, is that in the majority of the people who are dying with SCUBA gear or have accidents follow a very interesting pattern. They usually go down with their weight belt in place, vests uninflated, air in the tank, and frequently — most frequently — the regulator not in the mouth. Why this is taking place is something that — again, you'll hear some more on it tomorrow. It appears that some of these things are not equipment-related problems. This must go back to training and, in that framework, changing behavior to the point where the people will take advantage of the equipment capability they have to save their life.

Audience question: Are there any new developments in effective, inexpensive, underwater communication for Scuba divers?

Mr. Morgan: Well, I'm being kind of devious because I'm working very hard on that very thing, on the whole bit. I'm determined to sell enough of this gear. This is my retirement plan, see. If I tell enough people, then 50 percent of the divers are going to be communicating. Then, I'd better get off my rear and get the gear developed and try and sell it, and I hope you buy it. If it works, you'll buy it; and if it doesn't work, you won't.

Lt . Cdr. Thompson: We don't want to give away any secrets, but, you know, we're working on it now. But if we tell you everything we knew, you'd go out and make it, too.

Mr. Morgan: See, this is one of the big problems we were talking about. Funds are being spent by corporations or diving manufacturers.

Take a diving manufacturer who spends $10,000 to develop the perfect snorkel. How long do you think he will be on the market with a perfect unpatentable snorkel before the people that didn't spend the $10,000 in R & D will come up with it? Okay. The man who makes the decision to spend the $10,000 on R & D knows that he will be fighting an uphill battle. The only thing he'll have is the lead time in getting the thing on the market. Okay, this is fine for, say, $10,000. But suppose it's got to be a major expenditure of money, $100,000. He can't get enough lead time unless he can patent it and this is one of the very, very major problems in R & D in diving.

Dr. Egstrom: I had the opportunity not too long ago to do a review on underwater communication for a company which was going to go into the business. They were quite sure that with their technology and engineering background in communications, they could develop an inexpensive underwater communications systems for a diver. After doing the review literature, identifying the problems that were related with the development of this equipment, they decided to go into another line of work.

Dr. Bradner: I would like to stress or underline these remarks by saying the only thing that I've heard thus far this morning that I encourage you not to believe is Bev Morgan's comments about his own inventions. They work. Any of you who are turned on by making developments, or the idea of making developments, which are really needed, I would urge you to talk particularly with Tommy or Bev about these peripheral problems which really determine the success of it. Next question.

Audience question: How much can we be expected to pay for underwater communications gear?

Mr. Stewart: I've spent $5,000 on gear that doesn't work.

Mr. Morgan . . . The thing that I'm after is a $60 SCUBA diver communicator and I'm going to do it.

Audience question: How often is equipment a problem?

Dr. Bradner: I'm sure we've all been out with a novice diver who suddenly panics at 10 or 20 feet down because he gets a trickle of water in his mouth. I don't know whether to call this equipment or training, but I think I would concur with your estimate on it.

Lt. Cdr. Thompson: Hugh, may I make a comment on that before he goes? I have been fortunately or unfortunately — I don't know which it is — but I have been the chairman of this accident committee in Los Angeles County since its inception. Also, I worked for the coroner in Orange County. Never have I had an accident investigated that was the fault of the equipment. Maybe the way it was put together, the way it was put on the body, and the way it was used, but never the equipment. We washed the mucous and the sand out of it and turned it on. I'll give you an indication. We picked up a body from 1,300 feet that had been in the water for over a year by the growth on the tank. According to the marine biologist, there was 150 pounds of air in the tank and the regulator would still work.

Dr. Egstrom: I'd like to make one suggestion here, however. We've begun to see a great many of the people who are getting into trouble who get to the surface and are rejecting the regulator or the snorkel. Then they go into a hyperventilation syndrome — that's been described fairly well in the literature — and are drowning and going down very quickly. They're getting them in very shallow water and getting them back very fast. But, they're not able to resuscitate them. Part of this may be the result of having tried to move large volumes of air against the airway resistance either through the snorkel or the regulator. This may have been a contributor to the series of deaths that led to panic and ultimately disaster. In that case, I would feel that equipment does have some responsibility in the chain of circumstance.

Mr. Stewart: For those of you who are interested in accident reporting, we've had an accident report file here at Scripps since about 1957. This is not only an accident but an incidents report also. Whatever happens out of the ordinary, we have people write it up. We always have both buddies write it from their standpoint. They've done a pretty good job of evaluation in most cases; how they got into it, how they got out of it. That then becomes a part of the required reading for our next class. It makes pretty good reading. Here in San Diego we have a coroner's reporting situation similar to the one in L.A. It's only been in force a little over a year. Of the fatalities that we have had, none of these have been directly related to equipment other than the fact that people pulled Mae Wests and either pulled the bottles out of them, or they didn't detonate and they forgot to drop their weight belts. We picked up a man off the Coronado Islands who had been down a year and there was still air in the tank and the regulator worked after a year.

Audience question: Is equipment reliable?

Mr. Stewart: At the University we have to balance the dollar vs. efficiency, reliability and ease in maintaining a high standard of maintenance. Now, dollars being what they are, we pick and choose pretty well and our equipment has been very, very, very reliable. We've had no complaints at all along those lines.

Lt. Cdr. Thompson: The gist of the question that I have there is, why do manufacturers make and promote a full line of equipment although it may not be the best. We really can't say. I can't say. Egstrom can't say. You can't say. No one can say, this is the best snorkel or this is the best fin under all conditions. A snorkel that is good for Bev Morgan to swim two miles on the surface at a knot and a half is no good for a kid in the swimming pool. You have to look at the over-all market. The same thing in fins. The fin that perhaps will give you the best thrust would not be suitable for a youngster in the pool. Manufacturers, of course, have to look at it to try to cover all the bases, have anything that anyone wants to buy as long as it's safe. Now, I won't say a snorkel that has a eighth-inch bore to it is safe for a professional diver or any type of diver, but he should know better than to buy it, frankly. Although we're good guys, we're not in it to educate the whole world, really.

Dr. Bradner: Am I not right in recalling that the ping pong ball snorkel's been removed from the market even though it was very popular?

Lt. Cdr. Thompson: It's still there. You can still buy them. As the gentleman says, the 29-cent snorkel — except that inflation now makes it $1.50 — and you do see those so-called unsafe snorkels on the market.

Dr. Bradner: We had a recompression chamber here at one time. We abandoned it because we couldn't afford the manpower to keep it operative around the clock. Now, from that point, Jim, maybe you'd like to take it.

Mr. Stewart: We have the availability of the Navy very close at hand. I think that in the type of diving we do, you can assume an embolism to be the most critical thing that comes about. It's a go or no-go type thing. In the case of bends, I think that if we get a person in, we have an emergency procedure established, within the lifeguard service, within our own campus police, for immediate handling of such an accident. And we're probably, oh, 15 minutes from a chamber from the time we get the guy in from the pier. And then off we go.

Audience question: What do you do in a suspected "bends" case?

Mr. Stewart: We usually give him oxygen. It's all established — the format of handling any emergency — but I might say that in the past 10 years we've made some 28,000 accident-free dives. So, I think this controlled condition, really works out pretty well. We do have a chamber here on the campus that we choose to ignore. It's hooked up as an environmental test chamber; not as a treatment chamber. It might have treatment capabilities if we needed it, though.

Audience question: Are any first aid techniques for the "bends" being developed?

Dr. Egstrom: At the last International Conference on Underwater Education, we had a very excellent paper on first-aid for air embolism in the use of the Van Dalinberg position and some of these things. The basic problem is still the development of a first-aid technique that is going to be — that will be first-aid — something that anyone can do to help another person. At this point the thing you mentioned, the slant board, does not appear to be a satisfactory first-aid technique. Dr. Behnke and a number of others have urged the administration of 100 percent oxygen in instances where they have this and immediate transportation to a recompression chamber. Now, there are groups, the Virginia Mason Clinic, Dr. Cockett, and a number of others, who are trying to develop some first-aid capability which may involve the use of drugs, and plasma expanders and different kinds of things. I suspect that it will be a year or two or longer before we have that kind of capability if, in fact, we ever have it. So, the point, then, is that the recompression chamber will probably continue to be the only effective way of dealing with these problems. If we don't have the chambers, then we're going to continue to lose people.

Audience question: Where can chamber operating procedures be learned?

Lt. Cdr. Thompson: Many schools will teach it and, really, you don't have to be too sharp. In other words, you don't have to have a Ph.D. in chamber operation. When we donated one to the hospital at Avalon, I went out and trained the nurses, doctors and technicians, about 20 of them in one day. I go out about once a year now and spend a half a day with them for a refresher. You take a small chamber, a chamber that you can save a life or save some pain. You can learn to operate it very quickly.

Mr. Stewart: A matter of manual dexterity, more than anything.

Dr. Egstrom: There's a caution that has to be put in here, however. That caution is related to this thing. In many states (but not California) we have the Good Samaritan Law. If you're administering first-aid, you're protected from some kind of liability. Anytime that you involve yourself with a pressure chamber — and you can correct me if I'm wrong, Dr. Behnke — I believe you're practicing medicine. That necessarily has to be limited to those people who have insurance, to take care of the malpractice kinds of things that come into effect. That's outside the Navy. Inside the Navy it's quite a different problem.

Mr. Stewart: That's why we got out of the chamber business, just strictly from liability. We have a standard two-lock chamber and the University felt they couldn't afford the liability to run it.

Audience question: Is a list of chambers available?

Dr. Egstrom: It's already been done. The Los Angeles County Department of Parks and Recreation publishes a list that's available to anyone that wants it. I believe that in most of the areas you'll find little cards that have the recompression chambers and emergency numbers listed on them. These are available locally.

Audience question: Inaudible.

Dr. Egstrom: Reference: the decompression meter. The decompression meter has a micropore filter which can represent one critical tissue. If that critical tissue happens to be your critical tissue and the meter is calibrated properly, it should work for you. The difficulty that we run into, and one of the observations that I made to Mr. Stevenson, were the reports coming out of the Long Beach chamber. I believe either the last three or the last five people in the chamber all were using the meter, apparently incorrectly, and got into trouble. In one instance two divers, one meter, one got hit and one didn't. The meters had been involved in the last five problems that they had down there and that seems to indicate that improper use of the meter is extremely dangerous.

Dr. Bradner: I'd like to make an almost obvious point. Glen is referring to a particular commercially available decompression meter. The history of decompression computers extends back, oh, at least 20 years. In general, they turned out to be too expensive to be readily marketable. Hence, a simple single component unit which was cheap enough to be marketable is now the thing you're depending on. It is, again, not a recently conceived problem. There has been a very great deal of study on that particular question.

Mr. Morgan: I'd like to make a comment here because there's a great deal of truth in what Mr. Austin says. I don't want you to have the impression that I'm opposed to people using the meter. In fact, I favor using the meter for one very good reason. I know darn well they aren't going to work the repetitive dive problem. I figure that even if the meter is demonstrated to be somewhat inadequate, it's probably going to at least keep people thinking about decompression, paying attention to it, and in that respect it does serve a bit of deterrent capability. Now if people were properly trained, they would work their repetitive dive problems and they wouldn't have to use the meter. But the human being as he is, doesn't seem to want to do that. Therefore, the meter serves a definite purpose.

Dr. Bradner: It seems to me that we've got, if we push it hard, three minutes. Perhaps if I allow one minute to each of the other panelists to summarize the most significant thing that he notes this morning, then we should break for lunch and continue this informally. Jimmy, you want to start?

Mr. Sewart: Well, I think that it's been pretty well established that all of our feelings are the same. We have a great lack in bouyancy control, mobility as a function of rubber suit thickness vs. warmth, and communications. I think that these are the big areas that we must hit. I think that they're areas that are being looked at. And the response to this decompression meter thing, we have always insisted that two be used on a dive and we ride the hot one. Five of our divers using meters at 250′ for 10 minutes had two failures. One gauge did not go into decompression and one gauge "failed-safe" holding the diver for 12 minutes at 10 feet instead of seven. But no matter what the limitations are in diving we still get the job done.

Lt. Cdr. Thompson: The thing I'd like to close with is regardless of how good we make the equipment, we can never legislate against stupidity. As long as we have human beings, we're going to have stupidity.

Dr. Bradner: Bev, can you top that?

Mr. Morgan: There's got to be a way to get more funding for research and development or we'll never get better gear.

Physiologic Processes as Applied to Problems of Diving

Second Session

Speaker: **CDR. Bob Hoke, M. C.**
U. S. N., Naval Research Institute
Bethesda, Maryland

Panelists: **CDR. Robert C. Bornmann, M. C.**
U. S. N., Deep Submergence Systems Project
Chevy Chase, Maryland

Lt. CRD. Mark Bradley, M. C.
U. S. N., Submarine Development Group One
San Diego, California

CDR. James Vorosmarti, M. C.
U. S. N., Submarine Development Group One
San Diego, California

Chairman: **Dr. Hugh Bradner**
Scripps Institution of Oceanography
La Jolla, California

Physiologic Processes as Applied to Problems of Diving[1]

CDR Bob Hoke, MC, USN
Naval Medical Research Institute
National Naval Medical Center
Bethesda, Md.

INTRODUCTION

Throughout the literature in diving medicine and physiology one comes across the words "prevent" and "prevention". The operative philosophy behind much research in this field is fundamentally one of the preventive medicine — the maintenance of health and the prevention of disease. Progress in our ability to deal with the medical problems of underwater work and prevention of illness in divers calls for continued research with preventive intent, to study the origins of disorders, the basis of susceptibility or resistance to them, and ways to prevent them. Preventive medicine has traditionally used epidemiologic studies and diving medicine needs them too.

"Epidemiologic investigations should be of prime value in identification of susceptible persons and in disclosure of pathogenetic factors which convert the susceptible person, the potential case, into a frank case of disease."[1] Beyond this there is a need to determine the nature of the physiologic changes which deplete the natural protective reserve of the diver and which provide the setting for pathologic changes. Such knowledge will lead to effective ways to prevent injury to divers. One should always keep in mind that the man underwater is a "potential case."

In this way, diving physiology is more than a descriptive science. As the basic science for diving medicine, applied diving physiology has objectives that are consistently therapeutic — in the broad sense of the word "therapeutic" which, in modern medicine, includes treatments with a preventive objective.

[1] The opinions and assertions contained herein are those of the author and are not to be construed as official or as reflecting the views of the Department of the Navy or the Navy at large.

Each act of therapy, for a physician, has a subject, a target, and a purpose. The subject is a host who may be healthy or diseased; the target is a medical condition that may or may not be already present in the host, and the purpose is either to prevent a target from occurring in that host or to alter one that exists.[2] According to these purposes, then, the therapeutic objectives of applied diving physiology fall into two classes:

1) Starting with the healthy diver, the therapeutic objective is *preventive:* to prevent illness and serious adverse physiologic changes, e.g., decompression sickness.

2) Starting with a diver who is ill or who is in a dysfunctional condition, the therapeutic objective is *remedial:* to eliminate or modify that condition, e.g., to recompress the patient with decompression sickness. However, even in the case of the diseased diver there is an additional therapeutic objective which is basically preventive — to forestall the development of complications, e.g., to prevent chronic lung damage following pulmonary oxygen toxicity.

There is still much need for descriptive work in diving physiology. The literature grows each year, but the knowledge gained must still be applied to the healthy, working diver to keep him that way — in the water and after returning to the surface.

I would like to discuss diving physiology from two aspects. First, the problem areas and the preventive objectives in each area (Table 1), and secondly, the physiologic reactions to the stressors found in diving (Table 2).

Table 1

PROBLEM AREAS AND PREVENTIVE OBJECTIVES

A. Compression
   1. Squeeze
   2. Compression arthralgia
B. Decompression
   1. Alternobaric vertigo
   2. Overexpansion of lungs
   3. Decompression sickness and bubble formation
C. Oxygen at high pressure
   1. Acute central nervous system toxicity
   2. Pulmonary oxygen toxicity
   3. Hematologic changes
D. Inert gas at high pressure
   1. Nitrogen narcosis
E. Pulmonary ventilation
   1. Hypoxia
   2. Hypercapnia
F. Thermal balance
   1. Excessive heat loss.

Table 2

UNDERWATER STRESSORS

1. Immersion in cold water
2. Oxygen at high pressure
3. Inert gas at high pressure
4. Increased carbon dioxide
5. Decompression and bubble formation
6. Increased density of breathing media
7. Forced muscular exertion
8. Confinement and isolation
9. Darkness and danger

PROBLEM AREAS AND PREVENTIVE OBJECTIVES

Compression

1. *Squeeze:* In accordance with the pressure-volume relations of a gas, any air containing space within the body or formed at the body's surface must undergo a decrease in volume when the surrounding pressure increases. If it cannot change volume then it must admit gas under pressure to equalize with the ambient pressure, otherwise the resulting pressure difference causes tissue injury known as "squeeze." The membranes lining the cavity become engorged with blood and fluid and eventually bleeding takes place into the cavity. In this way the volume is decreased enough to equalize the pressure. The common sites of squeeze, familiar to all divers, are: the middle ear, sinuses, tooth fillings, eye goggles, and skin folds in dry suits. The middle ear and sinuses must be equalized by air going through the Eustachian tubes and sinus ostia.

To prevent squeeze, descend at a controlled rate to allow equilization and stop if pain occurs. Don't use ear plugs or allow wet-suit hood to occlude the external ear canal (this causes external ear squeeze). When using dry suits some form of volume replacement, as in the constant volume dry suit, is required. Don't dive with a cold. People with chronic sinusitis should avoid diving.

2. *Compression arthralgia:* This phenomenon is not a problem in ordinary diving but is one in deep diving, especially on rapid descents. In August, 1965, a 650 foot saturation dive was conducted by Ocean Systems Incorporated. The descent was made in one hour and during that descent both divers experienced pains and stiffness in some of their joints. They described the feeling as "arthritis," "no joint juice," or "joints cracking like rice crispies."[3] The discomfort persisted for several days.

Present day saturation dives use a much slower rate of descent, 12 hours to go 600 feet, to obviate this problem. This not only prevents compression arthralgia but hopefully helps to prevent tissue injury which could increase the risk of decompression sickness during ascent.

Decompression

1). *Alternobaric vertigo:* This problem was discussed by Lundgren[4] who surveyed 550 Swedish divers. He found that after excluding the obvious causes of dizziness, such as cold water entering the ear, impure air, nitrogen narcosis, decompression sickness and other medical problems, there were still many unexplained attacks of acute vertigo. This vertigo occurred during ascent, was more frequent following head colds, and could be induced by "popping" the ears. A relative overpressure in the middle ear is the most important factor.

Lundgren stated, "Obviously, serious vertigo is a grave menace to the diver. Vomiting while underwater could be fatal, while disorientation would be hazardous, especially if the air supply is exhausted."[4] Divers who are inclined to experience alternobaric vertigo should use nasal decongestants before diving and should never dive with a cold.

2. *Overexpansion of the lungs:* The pressure-volume relations which predict squeeze during descent also predict potential over-expansion of the lungs during ascent. A lung full of compressed air at 100 feet will fill four lungs full at the surface if no air were expelled. At some point during an ascent with air trapped in the lung by breathholding or laryngeal spasm, the lung tissues will become overexpanded. As a result air will leak out of the lungs into a) the thoracic cavity — causing pneumothorax b) the mediastinum — causing mediastinal emphysema and subcutaneous emphysema, c) the pulmonary blood vessels — causing air embolism.

Air embolism is the most dangerous, for the emboli travel quickly to the brain causing unconsciousness. If the diver does not subsequently drown as a result of becoming unconscious in the water, his life may be saved if prompt recompression is available. A woman's life was saved recently after several hours of delay between the air embolization and the treatment.[5]

This problem can be prevented only by proper training to exhale during any ascent when breathing compressed gas. Even then an occasional person may trap some air in a small section of the lung because of a ball-valve type mechanism. Exhaling properly won't prevent overexpansion of that segment. This is the reason that all divers need a large-size chest x-ray as part of their medical examination before being allowed to dive.

3. *Decompression sickness and bubble formation:* Decompression sickness is not the simple, homogeneous disease that most divers call "the bends." The bends is only one form of this many-faceted syndrome which can cause chronic disability and death as well as acute joint pain. It includes all the signs and symptoms and patho-physiologic processes which occur as a result of decreasing the hydrostatic pressure surrounding the body in such a fashion that inert gas is liberated into a gas phase within the body.

The most common and most characteristic symptom is pain, particularly joint pain, the *"bends."* It may come on gradually or be abrupt, severe, paroxysmal, aching, boring, associated with cold sweat, and made worse by movement. Exercise during or right after decompression may bring it on, as will a hot bath. Painful stiffness, tenderness, heat, and swelling may also be noted. The skin, though, may be cool and show a leaden hue, or conversely, it may show erythema, purplish mottling, bruise-like discolorations, and intense itching may be felt. Lymphatic occlusion with swollen nodes has been demonstrated.[6] Many years ago among tunnel workers epigastric pain and vomiting were frequently seen but are less common now. Neurologic signs and symptoms are legion: sensory disturbances, motor disturbances and paralysis, headaches, dizziness, incoherence, disturbances of speech and vision, deafness, convulsions mania, unconsciousness and sudden death. An elevated body temperature can occur and is easily misinterpreted as of infectious origin. The pulmonary form of decompression sickness, known as *"the chokes,"* is characterized by substernal distress aggravated by deep breathing which will usually cause coughing. When untreated it progresses to shock, coma and death. A delayed form of neurocirculatory collapse may also occur several hours after decompression. Finally, a chronic, long-delayed complication of decompression sickness is *aseptic bone necrosis.* Common in caisson workers, it is now being found in naval and civilian divers throughout the world.[7,8]

These symptoms and signs may occur during decompression, within a few minutes, or many hours after a dive. Ninety percent occur within three to six hours after surfacing.[9] They may occur after dives that fall within the no-decompression limits, or after dives in which careful decompression was given. And it is not surprising to find that an inadequate decompression does not inevitably cause decompression sickness. No correlation exists between the amount of decompression time missed and the severity of symptoms. One diver may miss 45 minutes and suffer joint pains, while another who misses only 10 minutes may be permanently paralyzed. A diver coming up from a deep dive on a long slow schedule (15 minutes per foot) suddenly suffered permanent hearing loss in one ear — which may or may not be due to decompression sickness.[10]

Liberated Bubbles

Factors which influence the incidence of decompression sickness are age, previous injury, obesity, excessive alcohol intake, loss of sleep, fatigue, exercise during decompression or immediately afterwards, diving in cold water, and anxiety. Practically anything which will impair or alter the circulatory efficiency of the body will influence the incidence of decompression sickness by changing the gas transport effectiveness.

The problem, of course, is to find a rational explanation that will satisfactorily account for all the observed events. Most experts since the time of Paul Bert[11] have regarded liberated bubbles as the etiologic agents of decompression sickness, with the signs and symptoms depending on the location of the bubbles in the body.

So, our essential preventive objective in decompression sickness is to prevent bubble formation. The only means currently utilized to accomplish this is with decompression schedules properly conceived and properly carried out. A decompression schedule is a therapeutic maneuver with *preventive* intent — not a remedial procedure. A good decompression schedule is the solution to the problem of how to safely eliminate the excess gas acquired at a certain depth and time. If the diver follows the wrong schedule, or no schedule at all, he is using the wrong solution to his problem.

Proper conception of decompression procedures is a crucial and complex matter, and theories abound. The current mathematical models for decompression differ in assumptions about: permissible tissue supersaturation diffusion versus perfusion limited processes in gas uptake and elimination and the nature of body tissues.[12] The models all have the same objective though — to keep the dissolved gas in solution.

To illustrate the influence of bubbles on the outcome of decompression, Kidd, at the Third Symposium on Underwater Physiology, told of an experience with an ultrasonic bubble detector.[13] During a chamber dive which took 12 hours to complete, he monitored one diver for six hours with no change in the signal on the detector — i.e., no bubbles. When he then put the device on the other diver who was complaining of skin itch he got a strong signal indicating bubbles. Within 10 minutes that diver had full blown decompression sickness, but his partner remained symptom free. This kind of experience makes one hope that decompression research can be conducted with a finer, more quantitative end point for detecting an inadequate decompression schedule than waiting for subjective symptoms to develop in the diver.

Oxygen at High Pressure

Oxygen is widely used in diving: to enhance inert gas elimination and shorten decompression times, for surface decompression, closed and semi-closed circuit scuba, and for treatment of decompression sickness and air embolism. It is the latent period before the onset of oxygen toxicity which allows it to be used but oxygen is always a potential problem. An important point to remember, though, is that oxygen toxicity is not limited to situations where 100 percent oxygen is breathed. The toxicity is related to its partial pressure and the length of exposure. Even compressed air can potentially cause oxygen poisoning on working dives beyond 250 feet.

There are several classical forms of oxygen toxicity of interest to divers:

1) *Acute, central nervous system toxicity:* At partial pressures above 1.6 ata, oxygen can cause convulsions if breathed long enough. The latent period is variable, but becomes shorter as the oxygen pressure increases.[14] Navy divers are required to pass an oxygen tolerance test of 30 minutes at 60 feet (2.8 ata). Convulsions are the *initial* symptom in only four percent of cases. Nausea, muscular twitching

and dizziness are commonly seen before seizures so they act as warning symptoms. Tunnel vision, tinnitus and paresthesias also occur.

Potentiators of acute oxygen poisoning are: exercise, increased carbon dioxide levels, wet exposures and increased ambient temperature. The latent period can be significantly prolonged by intermittent air breathing, a technique employed in the USN Treatment Tables 5 and 6 (the minimal-recompression oxygen-breathing tables).[15]

2). *Oxygen toxicity of the lung:* Although CNS effects can be prevented by keeping the partial pressure of oxygen down to 1.0 ata, there are still some important pulmonary effects. These effects limit the use of 100 percent oxygen for extended periods in decompression. After several hours of breathing oxygen by mask the respiratory passages are dry, the chest feels tight and the vital capacity is diminished.[16]

The pulmonary effects of oxygen at 1.0 ata occur in two distinct stages:[17] a) The acute exudative stage. This stage, which is reversible, occurs within four days in primates. The pulmonary arterioles become thickened and edema fluid accumulates around the vessels and in the alveoli. b) The subacute proliferative stage. If the exposure continues, a dangerous, irreversible stage of fibrous proliferation occurs in the alveolar walls, and death ensues.

3. *Hematologic changes:* With long term exposures to oxygen at partial pressures as low as 0.6 ata, as may occur with astronauts and hydronauts, hematologic changes are seen, consisting of hemolysis and progressive decline in red cell mass.[18] These changes are reversible.

Oxygen toxicity is preventable in diving if the exposure time and partial pressure of oxygen are controlled. Table 3 lists the current USN standards for oxygen partial pressures limits for working dives.

Table 3

OXYGEN PARTIAL PRESSURE LIMITS FOR WORKING DIVES

Exposure time (min)	pO_2 (ata)
30	1.6
40	1.5
50	1.4
60	1.3
80	1.2
120	1.1
240	1.0

Inert Gas at High Pressure

Nitrogen narcosis: Nitrogen, although chemically inert, has a profound effect at high pressures on the central nervous system. For experienced hard-hat divers the euphoria and progressive deterioration in performance due to nitrogen narcosis may be only a nuisance.

They have difficulty in remembering tasks, are quite clumsy, and they may even pass out while trying to finish a job. However, because they are still attached to, and are in communication with, the surface they can be recovered with little difficulty.

This is not the case with free-swimming SCUBA divers who risk their lives diving beyond 150 feet. When they become euphoric and lose their power of concentration they are also apt to lose all concern for personal safety. An unconscious SCUBA diver has one foot in the grave.

The phenomena that accompany *nitrogen narcosis* are depth related, and are given in Table 4.[19] These figures are only approximate since much depends on individual tolerance, anxiety, work, alcohol excess and general fatigue. Narcosis has been noted in a few persons as shallow as 30 feet.[20]

TABLE 4

NITROGEN NARCOSIS

100-150 feet. Light headed, increasing self confidence, loss of fine discrimination and some euphoria.

150-200 feet. Joviality and garrulousness. Perhaps some dizziness.

200-250 feet. Laughter may easily be uncontrolled and approach hysteria. Power of concentration is lessened and mistakes made in simple practical mental tasks. May be peripheral numbness and tingling. Less attention paid to personal safety. Delayed responses to signals and stimuli.

300 feet. Depression and loss of clear thinking. Impaired neuromuscular co-ordination. In addition there is the added danger of oxygen poisoning.

350 feet. Approaching unconsciousness.

On return to surface — Where there has been a considerable degree of narcosis, amnesia lasting for several hours may follow. Extreme sleepiness is very common.

From S. Miles, *Underwater medicine,* 3rd Edition, J. P. Lippincott, Philadelphia, 1969. p. 112.

The problem is to prevent serious deterioration of performance which accompanies nitrogen narcosis and to protect the diver from himself. There are several ways to do this. One way is to substitute helium for nitrogen, especially for dives beyond 200 feet. (However, there is some evidence that at depths beyond 1,000 feet helium, too, will have some narcotic effects.)[21] Training and experience help to increase a diver's tolerance to nitrogen narcosis. Since, in general, nitrogen narcosis cannot be circumvented in air diving, the best advice is to limit SCUBA divers to 130 feet, inexperienced hard-hat divers to 150 feet, and experienced ones to 250 feet. Because of the loss of memory and judgement, pre-dive planning is important. One should never dive alone.

Pulmonary Ventilation

When a diver goes underwater breathing compressed air, or any other mixture of gases, there are two essentials that his pulmonary ventilation must provide. The air going in must provide adequate oxygen for the work being done — to prevent *hypoxia.* The air coming out must efficiently remove the carbon dioxide being produced — to prevent *hypercapnia.* Inadequate pulmonary (alveolar) ventilation is the most prevalent disorder of pulmonary function in diving, according to Lanphier.[22]

Since it requires energy to move air through tubes, it requires a certain amount of work to ventilate the lungs. Ordinarily the oxygen consumed by the respiratory muscles is only a small fraction of the available oxygen. During exercise, though, the resistance in the airways increases and more oxygen is demanded by the respiratory muscles because of the increased ventilatory demand. This process can reach the critical stage where the work required to ventilate the lungs (the work of breathing) is consuming all the additional oxygen brought in by ventilation. If that happens, no other useful work is possible. So one needs to be able to predict this point if one plans to go deeper and deeper into the sea.

The problem is that the body's only defense against an increase in carbon dioxide (which happens with any exercise) is to increase the ventilation. When a further increase in ventilation is impossble, *hypercapna* and *carbon dioxide poisoning* are inevitable.

Two factors that increase the work of breathing are a poorly designed breathing apparatus, and the increase in gas density as pressure increases. A dense gas creates turbulent flow in the ventilatory passages which reduces the efficiency of ventilation and creates more breathing work. Anthonisen estimates that the lung ventilation required to sustain moderate exercise can be maintained when the breathing atmosphere is 15 times more dense than room air. This would be equivalent to breathing oxyhelium with a pO_2 of 0.3 ata at approximately 3,000 feet.[23]

Thermal Balance in Divers

The thermal problems of diving are receiving more recognition now. The ability of a diver to accomplish useful work may be just as limited by the problem of cold thermal stress as by any other problem. The preventive objective in this problem is to maintain the diver's body temperature.

Heat loss in the diver occurs by several mechanisms, but in ordinary circumstances most of the body heat lost in moderately cold water is through the trunk of the body.[24] Heat is conducted from the body organs through the trunk to the skin and lost from the skin by conduction and convection in the water. In a cold chamber, heat will be lost by radiation to the walls. These forms of heat loss are normally counteracted by increasing the insulation surrounding the diver, supplying him with some form of heat, and by heating the chamber.

In addition to these forms of heat loss, deeper divers are faced with considerable heat loss through their lungs. Cold inspired gas is heated to body temperature and humidified in the lungs and then exhaled. Consequently heat is extracted from the body by the way of the lungs. Respiratory heat loss is a function of the density of the gas and its specific heat. One can see that breathing helium, with its good thermal conductivity and high specific heat, on deep dives places a severe thermal drain on a diver.[25] It is possible that respiratory heat loss alone could be greater than the metabolic heat production of the body. This problem is under study now at various places to determine the requirement for heating the diver's breathing gas.

These problem areas are certainly not discrete areas. The interactions among them are numerous. For example, the depressive action of inert gases is potentiated by high oxygen tension, or breathing oxygen during decompression establishes a better gradient for inert gas elimination while at the same time reducing tissue perfusion. But to understand the interactions requires more knowledge of the physiologic processes behind the problems. These processes are often reactions to the stressors in the underwater environment. Table 2 lists some of these stressors. In the next section some of the physiologic processes involved will be discussed.

PHYSIOLOGIC PROCESSES

Physiologic Reactions to Underwater Stressors

1). *Immersion in cold water:* McCally said, "water immersion of human subjects, whether it be breathhold diving, head-out immersion, hard-hat or SCUBA diving, produces striking changes in body fluid composition and volume distribution."[26] The results will be dehydration and loss of circulating plasma volume (hemoconcentration). This diuresis can also be seen in dry chamber dives, and both wet and dry dives are associated with bradycardia.

A sudden immersion in cold water causes a severe, reflex hyperventilation which is uncontrollable and will prevent effective swimming. Healthy, strong swimmers have perished while attempting to swim short distances in icy water.[27]

Other physiologic responses to cold include *vasoconstriction* and reduced blood flow to the skin, increased metabolic heat production, and an increase in pulmonary ventilation. In addition, there is slowing of muscle contractions and loss of function in the cutaneous sense organs.

2. *Oxygen at high pressure.* Because of the latent period before the onset of oxygen toxicity, there is time for important physiologic reactions to occur. These reactions, although harmless is themselves, in concert with reactions to other stressors may become significant.

The increase in dissolved oxygen in the blood meets all the metabolic needs of the tissues so hemoglobin is not reduced. Consequently, there is no reduced hemoglobin to help transport carbon dioxide. This results in an increase in tissue carbon dioxide, a slight increase in venous carbon dioxide and a drop in venous pH. The respiratory center is stimulated by this acidosis and the resulting increase in ventilation reduces the arterial blood carbon dioxide which in turn causes cerebral vasoconstriction.[28]

In addition, a drop in pulse rate and a decrease in cardiac output create a reduction in tissue perfusion, an effect which must be considered when calculating decompression schedules. A reduction in perfusion means a reduction in ability to transport inert gas from the tissues to the lungs for elimination.[29]

3) *Nitrogen at high pressure.* The most devastating effects of high tensions of nitrogen are the psycho-physiologic effects such as euphoria, retardation of higher mental functioning, impaired neuromuscular coordination and progressive loss of consciousness. These effects are potentiated by increased oxygen and carbon dioxide. The mechanism behind these effects has to do with a slowing down of neural functioning due to a conduction deficiency in the brain.[30]

The other major consequence of high ambient pressure of inert gas is the accumulation of gas in the body fluids and tissues. This acquired gas will have to be eliminated during decompression.

4) *Carbon dioxide.* At low concentrations, carbon dioxide is a respiratory stimulant, but when its effective partial pressure is increased, this gas incites the General Adaptation Syndrome.[31] As the concentration of carbon dioxide rises the respirations become rapid and shallow, the pulse rate and blood pressure increase and a flush of vasodilatation is seen. Headache and vomiting occur, accompanied by loss of coordination and impaired mental ability. When the concentration of carbon dioxide in the inspired air is above 0.1 ata the toxic effects are severe: unconsciousness, paralysis of the respiratory and cardiac centers and death.

5) *Increased density of breathing gas.* The main effects of increased gas density are increased airway resistance, decreased ventilatory flow rates, marked increase in the work of breathing and consequent reduction in ventilatory efficiency. This results in a reduction of the maximum voluntary ventilation that a diver could sustain and gradual build-up of carbon dioxide.

At great depths, another important physiologic effect occurs that is partially related to the increased gas density: The *hypoxic crisis.* Chouteau[32] noted, while taking goats in stages to 3,000 feet, that at certain depths, even though oxygen was kept at 0.21 ata, the goats showed abnormal neurologic signs and collapsed. They revived in each case when the partial pressure of oxygen was increased. There seems, then, to be an impediment to oxygen diffusion in the lungs at extreme pressures.

Another effect of increased gas density is a large increase in respiratory heat loss. At depths around 850 feet, in 40°F water, there is conjecture that the rate of heat extraction from the lungs by the cold, dense helium will exceed the ability of the pulmonary blood flow to counteract it. The result would be not only loss of body heat but possible pulmonary damage.

6. *Decompression and bubble formation.* It is difficult to enumerate the *physiologic* effects of decompression because what is important

is the *pathologic* consequences of inadequate decompression and bubble formation. The most important consequence of a safe decompression is the creation of a state of gas supersaturation in the tissues and the gradual elimination of the excess gas without bubble formation.

With inadequate decompression the story is quite different. There are numerous pathophysiologic consequences of bubble formation. These effects are related to two aspects of bubbling: the *mechanical* effects, and the *biochemical* effects.

a) *The mechanical effects* depend on bubble location. *Intracellular* bubbles will cause disruption of the cell, loss of function, liberation of tissue enzymes and extrusion of fat emboli. *Extravascular* bubbles can act similarly and can also cause compression and stretching of vessels and nerves. *Intravascular* bubbles, as emboli, create a sequence of events: obstruction, stasis, ischemia, hypoxia, endema, hemorrhage and cell death.

b *The biochemical effects* of bubbles relate to the gas-blood interface of the bubble and its surface-active properties. Platelets and fibrin adhere to the surface of bubbles. These platelet aggregates may release clotting factors leading to the formation of thromboemboli and may release catecholamines causing vasoconstriction.[33] Bubbles might also activate the early stages of blood coagulation through the Hageman factor and initiate disseminated intravascular coagulation.[34] Or they might trigger localized brady-kinin release.[35] The evidence from bubble oxygenators used in cardiopulmonary bypass suggests that bubbles in contact with blood induce a change in blood lipids which stimulates formation of fat emboli as well as thromboemboli.[36]

The evidence for direct mechanical effects of bubbles is classical and simple. A long line of investigators have observed and counted bubbles, most recently Buckles using the hamster cheek pouch and a pressurized optical bench.[37] Recompression is all that is required for most cases of decompression sickness. No theory other than the bubble theory accounts so well for the success of recompression.

The evidence for biochemical effect of bubbles is more indirect and is based on observation of drugs which decrease the severity and incidence of decompression sickness: heparin and other lipemia clearing drugs.[38,39,40] Low molecular weight dextran,[41] and antibradykinin drugs[35] have been found to improve the clinical outcome of decompression sickness. Much work is yet to be done on this aspect of decompression and the physiologic consequences of bubble formation.

Other stressors in the underwater environment which could be discussed are: forced muscular exertion, lack of food and water for several hours, confinement, isolation, darkness, and danger.

Individual Physiologic Variability

Superimposed on the various physiologic reactions to the stressors in the underwater environment in the whole subject of individual physiologic variability. Physiologic individuality is expressed in morphologic dimensions, in bodily processes, and in behavior. Physiological individuality relates to the individuality of the physical and chemical properties of the internal environment and to the functioning of organs and organ-systems responsible for physiological regulations.[42] The human is a constantly changing complex of processes, particularly observable when stressors are imposed. A man is not one mass of tissue with mathematical compartments that can always be described in the same manner.[13] There are two major categories of variability:

1) Individual differences: The factors that make each one of us distinct from all others. Many of our differences are rooted in genetics,[43] some are environmental,[44] and still others have an emotional and sociopsychologic basis.[45] Age, sex, body type, likes, dislikes, and habits are distinct for all of us.

2. Temporal variations: The physiologic factors in any one person that vary with the passage of time. One encounters repetitive sequences of events in his body which have varying cyclic periods ranging from a few hours to several months.[46,47] Sargent said, "First, the organism is a different biochemical, physiological and behavioral system at every hour and every season. Second, a stressor or stimulus of whatever kind will have different effects depending upon the phase when the organism encounters it."[48]

An environmental stressor, or hazard, may be more or less harmful, then, according to the periodic phase in the person exposed to that stressor. A practical example of this was given by the recent change in saturation decompression schedules by the Deep Submergence System Project. Because gas transport is less efficient during sleep, the decompression is halted for six hours each night and two hours each afternoon.[49]

The Influence of Preceding Physiologic Experience

How important, in diving physiology, is the physiologic experience of the preceding few hours before the dive, or before the decompression? It has been known for years that loss of sleep, excessive alcohol intake, fatigue, poor nutritional state and anxiety predispose a diver to decompression sickness. Also it is known that tunnel workers clearly exhibit acclimatization to decompression, as shown by decreasing incidence of bends as they are on the job longer.[50] This acclimatization is lost if they are off work for a week, so preceding physiologic experience is important.

Non-specific Reactions to Stressors

We have seen that there are many specific stressors in diving, each with a set of complicated and interrelated responses. Over the past 30 years, the work of Hans Selye[51] on the physiology and pathology of exposure to stress has shown that there is a large, nonspecific component to stress reactions. An organism tends to respond in a stereotyped manner to many stressor agents: trauma, extreme heat or cold, forced muscular exertion, intoxications, infections, intense light or sound, hemorrhage, and injections of various drugs.

Each of these stressors has some specific direct effects but, just as importantly, they all place the body in a "state of stress." The word *stress* indicates the body's emergency mobilization of hormones in response to external or internal stressors in order to achieve adaptation or promote defense. In the final outcome the specific reactions to stressors are superimposed on the general, non-specific pattern.

Stress initiates a dual chain of events in the body. One type of reaction leads to *damage,* probably through toxic metabolites, neural stimuli, or tissue deficiencies. The other chain is concerned with *defense* and is mediated by hormones from the pituitary and adrenal glands. Reactions to stressors are not just related to the quantities of steroid hormones but to the body's *sensitivity* to them. "Conditioning factors" such as heredity, pre-existing organ lesions, diet, previous exposures to stressors, and basal metabolic rate can alter the sensitivity of certain target organs (the joints, for example) to the effects of stressors.

Normally, in the books and articles on diving physiology, these problems and processes are all discussed separately which makes it difficult to appreciate the integrative processes going on behind them. The response to stressful conditions involves the entire body economy but is centered around the actions of the hypophyseal-adrenocortical system.[52] But neural integration of complex physiologic processes in humans also involves the cerebral cortex. It is the whole person who dives, not just a heart, two lungs, and some other organs and tissues.

Another phenomenon related to stress physiology (one which the behavioral scientists will perhaps comment upon) has to do with the influence of psychic states on physiologic processes. Grace *et al*[53] pointed out that the *meaning* which a stressful situation has for the subject will alter the observed physiologic response. They observed men who had a portion of their large bowel exposed. During times of relative tranquility the large bowel is pink. If the subject is depressed it looks pale and relaxed. If he is angry the bowel appears dark red, contracted and hypermotile. To illustrate how the same stressor can elicit different physiologic responses they placed a thumb screw-screw on each subject's head and tightened it. One man's bowel became pale and relaxed while another's became red and contracted under the same circumstances. Obviously, then, the situation had a different meaning to each of these men, and the consequence was a different physiologic response.

In the diving environment, the question is this: Would the rate of uptake and elimination of gas in the body be influenced by the psychophysiologic response to the meaning of a given situation to the individual diver? It appears, then, that the integration of the different physiologic processes of importance in diving is a highly complex phenomenon, but one whch must be kept in mind during the study of diving physiology.

REFERENCES

[1] Francis TJ: Research in preventive medicine. *JAMA* 172:993-999, 1960.

[2] Feinstein AR: Clinical epidemiology I: The populational experiments of nature and of man in human illness. *Ann Int Med* 69:807-820, 1968.

[3] Hamilton RW, MacInnis JB, Noble AD et al: *Saturation Diving at 650 Feet.* Tonawanda, NY, Ocean Systems, Inc., 1966.

[4] Lundgren CE: Alternobaric vertigo — a diving hazard. *Brit Med J* 2:511-513, 1965.

[5] Cockett ATK, Saunders JC, Pauley SM: Combined treatment (dextran and recompression) in decompression sickness. In, *Proceedings of the Fourth International Congress on Hyperbaric Medicine,* Sept 1969 (in press).

[6] Kidd DJ, Elliott DH: Clinical manifestations and treatment of decompression sickness in divers, pp 464-490 in, Bennett PB, Elliott DH (eds): *The Physiology and Medicine of Diving and Compressed Air Work.* Baltimore, The Williams and Wilkins Co., 1969.

[7] Elliott DH, Harrison JB: Aseptic bone necrosis in naval divers. In, *Proceedings of the Fourth Symposium on Underwater Physiology,* June 1969 (in press).

[8] Uhl RR: Aseptic bone necrosis in divers. *Aerospace Med* 39:1345-1347, 1968.

[9] Rivera J: Decompression sickness among divers; An analysis of 935 cases. *Mil Med* 129:314-334, 1964.

[10] Rubenstein CJ, Summitt JK: Vestibular derangement in decompression. *Proc 4th Symp Underwat Physiol* (in press).

[11] Bert P: *Barometric Pressure (1878).* Columbus, Ohio, College Book Co., 1943.

[12] Workman RD: American decompression, pp 252-290 in, Bennett and Elliott (eds): *op cit,* 1969.

[13] Lambertsen CJ (chairman), Kidd DJ et al: Panel on potential advances in deep diving, pp 312-326 in, Lambertsen CJ (ed): *Proceedings of the Third Symposium on Underwater Physiology.* Baltimore, The Williams and Wilkins Co., 1967.

[14] Donald KW: Oxygen poisoning in man. *Brit Med* J 1:688-717, 1947.

[15] Goodman MW, Workman RD: Minimal-recompression oxygen-breathing approach to treatment of decompression sickness in divers and aviators. Washington, DC, EDU Research Report 5-65, 1965.

[16] Clark JM, Lambertsen CJ: Pulmonary oxygen tolerance and the rate of development of pulmonary oxygen toxicity in man at two atmospheres inspired oxygen tension, pp 439-451 in, Lambertsen (ed): *op cit,* 1967.

[17] Robinson FR, Sopher RL, Witchett CE et al: Pathology of normobaric oxygen toxicity in primates. *Aerospace Med* 40:879-884, 1969.

[18] Fischer CL: Effects of oxygen on blood formation and destruction. *Proc 4th Symp Underwat Physiol* (in press).

[19] Miles S: *Underwater Medicine 3rd ed.* Philadelphia, JB Lippincott, Co., 1969, p 112.

[20] Kiessling RJ, Maag CH: Performance impairment as a function of nitrogen narcosis. Washington, DC, EDU Research Report 3-60, 1960.

[21] Bennett PB: Inert gas narcosis, pp 155-182 in Bennett and Elliott (eds): *op cit,* 1969.

[22] Lanphier EH: Pulmonary function, pp 58-112 in, Bennett and Elliott (eds): *op cit,* 1969.

[23] Anthonisen NR, Bradley ME, Vorosmarti J et al: Mechanics of breathing with helium-oxygen and neon-oxygen mixtures in deep saturation dives. *Proc 4th Symp Underwat Physiol* (in press).

[24] Keatinge WR: *Survival in Cold Water.* Oxford, Blackwell Scientific Publications, 1969, p 17.

[25] Rawlins JSP, Tauber JF: Thermal balance at depth. *Proc 4th Symp Underwat Physiol* (in press).

[26] McCally M: Body fluid volumes and the renal response of human subjects to water immersion. AMRL-TR-65-115, 1965.

[27] Keatinge WR, Prys-Roberts C, Cooper KE et al: Sudden failure of swimming in cold water. *Brit Med J.* 1:480-483, 1969.

[28] Lambertsen CJ: Effects of oxygen at high pressure, pp 1027-1046 in, *Handbook of Physiology: Respiration Vol. 2.* Washington, DC, American Physiological Society, 1964.

[29] Workman RD: Calculation of decompression schedules for nitrogen-oxygen and medium-oxygen dives. Washington, DC, EDU Research Report 6-65, 1965.
[30] Bennett PB, Ackles KN, Cripps JJ: Effects of hyperbaric nitrogen and oxygen on auditory evoked responses in man. *Aerospace Med* 40:521-525, 1969.
[31] *Submarine Medicine Practice* (NAVMED-P 5054). Washington, DC, Government Printing Office, 1956.
[32] Chouteau J: Respiratory gas exchange in animals during exposure to extreme pressures. *Proc 4th Symp Underwat Physiol* (in press).
[33] Philip RB: Personal communication.
[34] Hardaway RM: *Syndromes of Disseminated Intravascular Coagulation.* Springfield, Ill, Charles C Thomas, 1966.
[35] Chryssanthou C et al: Studies on dysbarism: II. Influence of bradykinin and bradykinin antagonists on decompression sickness in mice. *Aerospace Med* 35:741-746, 1961.
[36] Clifton EE: Hypercoagulability and the hemorrhagic state with extra-corporeal circulation. *Bibl haemat* 29:841-857, 1968.
[37] Buckles RG: The physics of bubble formation and growth. *Aerospace Med* 39:1062-1069, 1968.
[38] Barthelmy L: Blood coagulation and chemistry during experimental dives and the treatment of diving accidents with heparin, pp 46-56 in, Lambertsen CJ, Greenbaum LJ (eds): *Proceedings of the Second Symposium on Underwater Physiology.* Washington, DC, NAS/NRC Publication No. 1181, 1963.
[39] Philp RB: The ameliorative effect of heparin and partially depolymerized hyaluronate in decompression sickness in rats. *Can J Physiol Pharmacol* 42:819-829, 1964.
[40] Pauley SM, Cockett ATK: Role of lipids in decompression sickness. *Aerospace Med* 41:56-60., 1970.
[41] Cockett ATK: Physiological factors in decompression sickness. *Arch Env Health* 11:760-764, 1965.
[42] Sargent F, Weinman KP: Physiological individuality. *Ann NY Acad Sci* 134:696-719, 1966.
[43] Williams RJ: *Biochemical Individuality: The Basis for the Genetotropic Concept.* NY, John Wiley and Sons, Inc., 1956.
[44] Dubos R: *Man Adapting.* New Haven, Yale University Press, 1965.
[45] Lidz T: *The Person: His Development Throughout the Life Cycle.* NY, Basic Books, Inc., 1968.
[46] Halberg F: Temporal coordination of physiologic function. *Cold Springs Harbor Symp Quant Biol* 25:289-310, 1960.
[47] Richter CP: Biological clocks in medicine and psychiatry: Shock-phase hypothesis. *Proc Nat Acad Sci (USA)* 46:1506-1528, 1960.
[48] Sargent F: Concepts of human adaptability relevant to environmental epidemiology. *Am J Pub Health* 58 1638-1652, 1968.
[49] Bornmann, RC: Physiological considerations for deep helium-oxygen saturation diving. Paper presented to Marine Technology Society Symposium, Washington, DC, Oct 1969.
[50] Walder DN: Adaptation to decompression sickness. *Biometeorology* 2 (pt 1): 350-359, 1967.
[51] Stelye H: *The Physiology and Pathology of Exposure to Stress.* Montreal, Acta, Inc., 1950.
[52] Bajusz E: Pituitary-adrenocortical system: Its regulative and adaptive functions, pp 89-145 in, Bajusz E (ed): *Physiology and Pathology of Adaptation Mechanisms: Neural-Neuroendocrone-Humoral.* NY, Pergamon Press, Inc., 1968.
[53] Grace WJ, Wolf S, Wolff HG: *The Human Colon: An Experimental Study Based on Direct Observations of Four Fistulous Subjects.* NY, Hoeber, 1951.

REACTION 1
Second Session

CDR Robert C. Bornmann, MC, USN[1]
Deputy Assistant for Medical Effects

Deep Submergence Systems Project (PM11)
Chevy Chase, Md.

U.S. Navy Experiences with Decompression from Deep Helium-Oxygen Saturation Excursion Diving

I was in a quandary about a month ago when, having accepted an invitation to respond to today's principal paper, I realized that Dr. Hoke's very thorough presentation would leave little room for any reply which I could be sure would be of interest to this audience. About that time Professor James Mayer of CALTECH visited me in Washington. We had a fine morning together and he left me with the thought that perhaps I could respond with a discussion of decompression. The excellent paper of Dr. Hemmingsen,[(5)2] from here at Scripps, on supersaturation of gases in water, which was published at that time in SCIENCE suggested further that I might myself learn something if I brought the subject up for discussion in San Diego.

That paper referred to Haldane which is also the start of the story of decompression, and I will begin there. Dr. John Scott Haldane, not to be confused with his son, Dr. John Burdon Sanderson Haldane, was a Scot, a physician, and a physiologist. He was also honorary professor of mining at Birmingham University and, not incidentally, president of the Institute of Mining Engineers from 1924 to 1928 — a significant honor for a physiologist. Many of the most difficult problems in diving today would be solved if engineers and physiologists could follow his example and work more closely together.

In 1906, when Dr. Haldane was asked by the Admiralty to sit on a committee to investigate the problems of deep diving, decompression was an empirical process. There were a number of radically different theories of decompression, all highly touted by their scientific backers.

---

[1] The opinions and assertions contained herein are the private one's of the author and are not to be construed as official or reflecting the views of the Navy Department or the naval service at large.

[2] Refers to numbered bibliography at end of paper.

The success of a procedure in a limited operation was hailed as proof as its theoretical basis. Then as now, however, a procedure may work very well when followed exactly within the framework of its safe demonstration but not for the reasons claimed. The test of scientific basis is whether the principles espoused to explain what is happening will work as well when extended to further situations. Dr. Haldane was quick to point out when he published his tables[4] that they had been proved valid for the depths and times listed, but no statement could be made beyond that. The decompression procedure in use before Haldane was generally a slow continuous ascent from the surface. As Haldane pointed out in his report, the method unnecessarily prolonged the diver's time at higher pressures and thereby actually lengthened the decompression which was necessary. I except saturation diving as a special case.

Haldane did three things which revolutionized diving decompression. It has always surprised me that, although two of his methods are still in use today, he is remembered most often for an idea which is not universally applicable: the Haldane 2 to 1 ratio. First, he assumed a mathematical model of the body to be made up of a number of "half-time tissues" in which the tissue half-saturation time, the time to take up 50 percent of the amount of inert gas lacking for complete sauration, ranges from very fast to very slow depending upon the variations of perfusion efficiency to gas solubility. Simultaneous solutions for a limited number of half-saturation times is felt to be sufficient to define the range.

In descriptive terms the diver breathes gas at ambient pressure into his lungs. Molecules diffuse through the lung membrane to pass into solution in the blood. The blood is pumped out and perfuses the rest of the body where its dissolved gases can diffuse into the tissues. Events occur in reverse order to carry excess tissue gas back to the lung.

Although diffusion of gas molecules must occur at two places in this process, in the general case perfusion (or blood flow) is considered to be rate limiting. This is why half time longer than would be predicted necessary by diffusion analysis have been considered in decompression.

In whole body terms although the total volume of gas dissolved is a function of specific solubility, the rate at which any gas enters the body and approaches saturation is constant and independent of molecular size.[6] The amount of dissolved gas which any lesser portion of the body can hold also depends on solubility, yet the rate at which it accumulates depends upon perfusion or the rate at which it is transferred to that area.

Since blood supply varies dynamically, any specific anatomic site can have a variable half-time. Similarly the same anatomic site can have different half-times for different inert gases depending upon their solubility characteristics.

The point is that the half-time model is a mathematical one, which is useful to summarize or generalize the body. It is not an anatomically descriptive model.

Figure 1 shows a single exponential curve which, so long as the pressure remains constant, represents the inert gas exchange in any tissue. The ordinate is F or "time function" but is really percent of change. The abscissa is simply time.

P_T is partial pressure of inert gas in the tissue at any time T
P_O is original partial pressure of inert gas in the tissue
P is partial pressure of inert gas in the lungs
and

$$P_T = P_O + F\,(P - P_O)$$

The time function (F) is defined as

$$F = 1\tfrac{1}{2}U \qquad \text{where } U = T/H$$

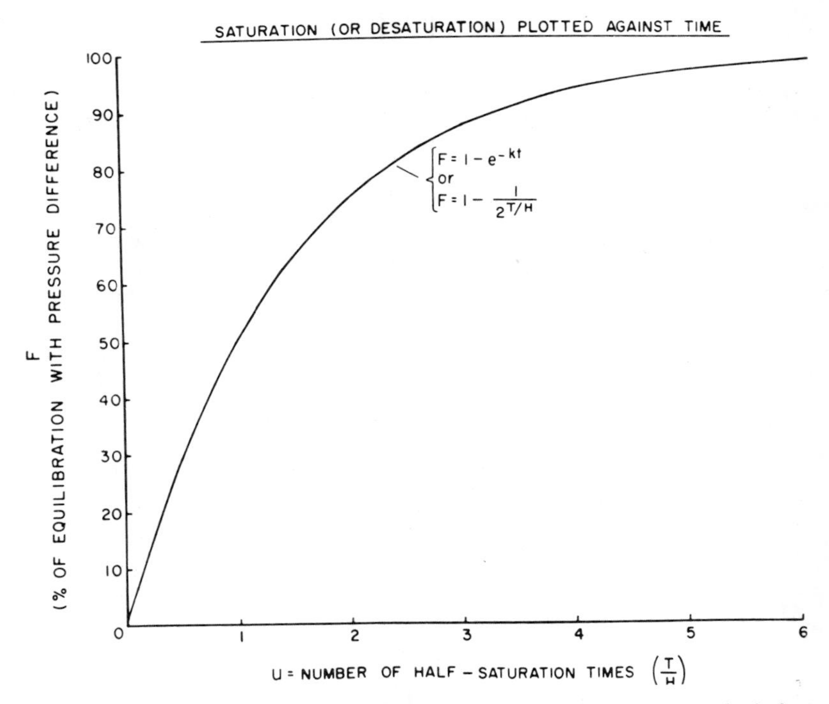

Figure 1: **Increase in inert gas tension in any theoretical mathematical tissue as a function of time.**

The pressure change to be calculated is the change, from the tissue tension at the beginning of any interval, toward saturation with inert gas at its partial pressure in the diver's breathing gas. This is itself the product of total pressure times proportion of inert gas in the breathing mixture. To start with the easiest case, a diver leaves the surface saturated with air at one atmosphere and descends to the bottom breathing air at increased pressure. The DELTA P, or pressure differential, is then the difference between the bottom pressure and one atmosphere. However, almost immediately the different rates of buildup will create different tensions in different half-time tissues. For example a 20-minute dive will create a change of 4U in the five minute tissue, 2U in the 10 minute tissue, 1U in the 20 minute tissue, ½U in the 40 minute tissue. These fractions of the pressure difference will be added to one atmosphere to give the varying tissues tensions at the end of the bottom time which will also then be the tensions at the beginning of the ascent. A negative value for (P minus P_0) indicates the loss of inert gas in outgassing. Six U (98½%) is considered a practical limit for "saturation."

Figure 2 is taken from the *Report of the Admiralty Committee on Deep Water Diving*[4] and shows Haldane's solution for the amount of air dissolved in the 5, 10, 20, 40 and 75 minute "half-time tissues" during a 16 minute dive to 168 feet and decompression according to his new stage method, which was the second contribution. This made the fullest use of the permissible difference in pressure between tissue gas tension and hydrostatic pressure to hasten the elimination

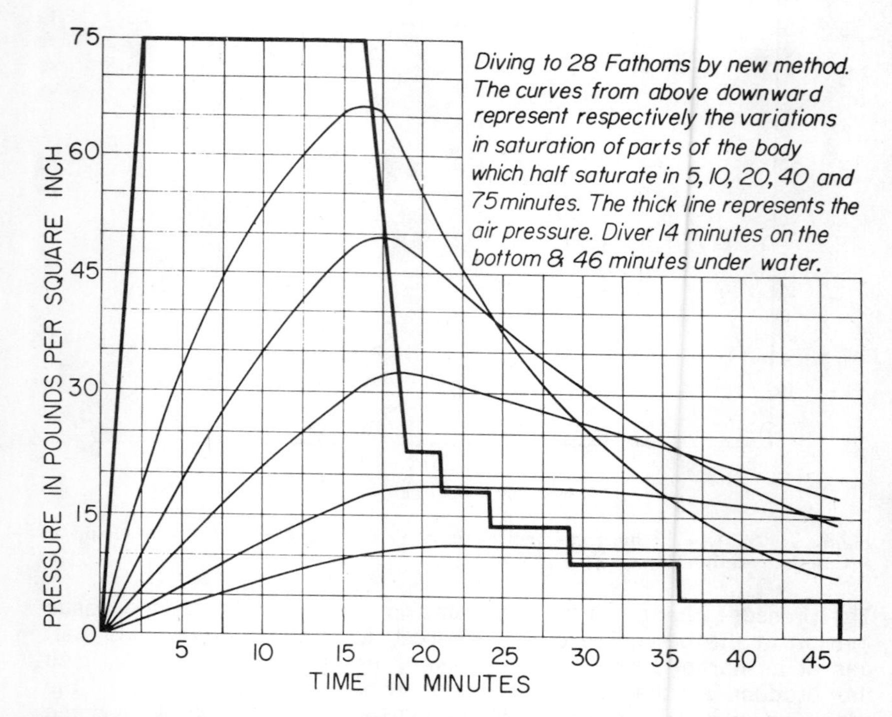

Figure 2: **Haldane's original analysis of change in tissue tensions of air during 16 minute air dive to 168 feet(4).**

of nitrogen from the diver's body. Finally, Haldane's concept of a 2:1 ratio for safe supersaturation in ascent was a brilliant and extremely useful one as it permitted formulation of the first practical and safe decompression tables. However, it is valid only in a limited case and has not proved safe for long and deeper exposures. Haldane himself stated in his first report that the validity of the ratio for pressure much in excess of six atmospheres was doubtful, as no experimental data existed, and later that for air dives exceeding six atmospheres absolute some reduction of the ratio is required. Later work in the U. S. Navy demonstrated that surfacing ratios increased as the half-saturation time decreased, to 3.8:1 for the five minute half-time tissue, and that permissible ratios also decreased with depth. Development of diving with helium-oxygen mixtures focused attention on the ratio of inert gas partial pressures to ambient pressure rather than the ratio of total pressures. The same mathematical model can be used for air and for helium-oxygen, but a different set of ratios and significant half-times will result in different decompression schedules. More recently Workman found it more convenient to work with maximum tissue pressures rather than ratios.[7]

I shall not attempt to describe to you today the perplexing situations which the Navy has faced in the last four years in its attempts to develop safe operational schedules for decompressing from relatively short dives (30 to 90 minutes) to moderate depths (300 to 450 feet). I can make my point more clearly and easily with saturation diving examples. In my opinion, all diving deeper than 250 feet in

TABLE 1

RATE OF ASCENT	15 MIN/FT or 4FT/HR
	450 FEET
	350 FEET
	250 FEET
FOUR HOUR STOPS AT	150 FEET
	100 FEET
	50 FEET

Saturation decompression schedule used in SEALAB III, a 600 foot saturation dive.

the future for more than moderate work times (five man-hours) will use saturation-excursion techniques. In saturation diving the diver's body is saturated with the gases of his pressurized environment at the partial pressure which they exert in the atmosphere of his habitat. The most slowly desaturating tissue should then control the ascent in decompression all the way to the surface. If our theories had been correct, the most efficient way to accomplish this would be to regulate the ascent at a constant rate which is a function of the body's slowest tissue.

In a paper written in 1966[2] I presented some calculations for the saturation situation and concluded that if a 180 minute tissue was the slowest that must be considered then ascent could be made at 8½ minutes per foot (under the conditions of the dive described). If a slower tissue existed then ascent must be slower: 11.3 mpf for 240, 14.1 mpf for 300, and 16.9 mpf for the 360 minute half-saturation time tissues. I also described some of the difficulties which had arisen as saturation dives went deeper and total decompression lengthened. Slower tissues were postulated and ascent rate was slowed. By the time we had progressed to making 600 foot saturation dives we had slowed the ascent rate to 15 minutes per foot and arbitrarily added four hour stages of no change in pressure.

Table I shows the decompression schedule used for SEALAB III as typical of this format. In 1969, however, we ran a long series of saturation dives to test our new excursion tables. This format was not adequate to provide for uncomplicated final decompression in these tests. We therefore changed the format for final decompression to that shown in Table II. The ascent was continuous during the two eight hour periods of ascent, but a two-hour stage in the middle of the afternoon and a six-hour overnight stage of no pressure change was included. Table III shows that we had decided to use different rates of ascent depending upon the depth range, with the speed of decompression slowing as the diver approaches closer to the surface.

TABLE 2

0600 to 1400	8 Hours	I	ASCENT
1400 to 1600	2 Hours	II	STOP
1600 to 2400	8 Hours	III	ASCENT
2400 to 0600	6 Hours	IV	STOP

Standard Daily Schedule for decompression from saturation dive now in standard use in the U.S. Navy.

TABLE 3

DEPTH RANGE	RATE OF ASCENT	
600 to 200 Feet	10 min/ft or	6 ft/hr
200 to 100 Feet	12 min/ft	5 ft/hr
100 to 50 Feet	15 min/ft	4 ft/hr
50 to surface	20 min/ft	3 ft/hr

Rates of ascent used with the Standard Daily Schedule for saturation decompression.

The final rate of 20 minutes per foot could indicate that a tissue with a half-time slower than 400 minutes exists to control decompression.

However, the saturation diving program in which this happened was designed to test new excursion schedules. The excursion schedules were basically computed on a 200 and 240 minute half-saturation time tissue. That test program was an outstanding success. Eleven hundred excursion dives were made from saturation exposures at 150, 200, 300, 350, 500 and 600 feet without one sign of decompression inadequacy.[3]

According to the present Navy standard table for helium-oxygen SCUBA diving from the surface it is possible to make a 60 minute no-decompression dive to 80 feet, and a 35 minute no-decompression dive to 100 feet. According to Table IV if one makes an excursion from a saturation dive as deep as 150 feet it is possible to go 75 feet deeper for a 150 minute no-decompression dive. Or, the excursion diver can stay for as long as 60 minutes 100 feet deeper than his saturation exposure and make a no-decompression return to his original depth. Table V is used for saturation dives at 300 feet or deeper and it permits no-decompression excursions for 100 minutes 100 feet deeper than the saturation depth, or 60 minutes at an excursion depth of 150 feet deeper. Repetitive excursions are possible with the use of Table VI, which gives appropriate credit for any decompression which takes place in the habitat between excursions.

Calculations for these tables were performed in the method which I have just described, except that only the slowest tissues had to be considered. Uptake of gas in an excursion was calculated at a 200 minute half-time rate. Desaturation in the habitat was calculated conservatively at a 240 minute half-time rate. This is almost a linear increase and computation of the tables was relatively easy. Proof of the tables at any saturation depth should constitute proof that they

TABLE 4

DEPTH OF EXCURSION FROM SATURATION EXPOSURE	NO DECOM-PRESSION LIMITS (Min.)	REPETITIVE GROUP DESIGNATION					
		A	B	C	D	E	F
PLUS 25 FEET		60	150	300	600		
50	270	30	60	100	150	210	270
75	150	20	40	65	90	120	150
100	60	10	20	30	40	50	60

No-Decompression limit Table, repetitive Group Designation Table, and Repetitive Excursion for excursions from Saturation Exposure at a depth between 150 feet and 300 feet of Seawater Gauge Depth.

TABLE 5

DEPTH OF EXCURSION FROM SATURATION EXPOSURE	NO DECOM-PRESSION LIMITS (Min.)	REPETITIVE GROUP DESIGNATION					
		A	B	C	D	E	F
PLUS 25 FEET	–	60	150	300	600		
50	270	30	60	100	150	210	270
75	150	20	40	65	90	120	150
100	100	15	30	45	60	80	100
125	75	10	20	30	45	60	75
150	60	10	20	30	40	50	60

No-Decompression Limit Table, Repetitive Group Designation Table, and Repetitive Excusion Timetable for excursions from Saturation Exposure at a depth between 300 feet and 600 feet of Seawater Gauge Depth.

TABLE 6

REPETITIVE GROUP AT THE BEGINNING OF THE HABITAT INTERVAL (FROM PREVIOUS EXCURSION)	REPETITIVE GROUP AT THE END OF THE HABITAT INTERVAL (BEFORE REPETITIVE EXCURSION)					
	F	E	D	C	B	A
F	TO 1:00	2:30	4:00	6:30	12:00	24:00
E		1:30	3:00	5:30	10:00	24:00
D			2:00	4:00	8:00	24:00
C				2:30	6:30	24:00
B					4:00	24:00
A						24:00

Habitat Interval Credit Table for Saturation Exposure at a depth between 600 feet of Seawater Gauge Depth.

were safe for use from any deeper depth. The difficult decision was to choose the shallow saturation depth at which to conduct definitive testing.

Figure 3 is a graphical display of the change in M values with increasing depth to simplify determination of shallow limits for these no-decompression excursions. Absolute depth has been subtracted from the M value figures given in Workman's original table. They are expressed instead as the maximum increase in tissue helium tension above hydrostatic pressure which is permitted in supersaturation at that depth. The right hand scale is always 10 feet greater than that on the left, and expresses the increase in tissue helium tension which still permits a no-decompression return to a saturation exposure in which the oxygen partial pressure is controlled at 0.3 ATA or 10 feet of seawater. As stated earlier with the slowing of tissue half-saturation times the surfacing value decreases and the rate of increase with depth lessens. The 200 and 240 minute M values are always 20 feet above absolute hydrostatic pressure and do not increase with depth. They have a flat slope.

The bar diagram at the right in Figure 3 shows the increases in all representative half-time tissues during a 60-minute no-decompression excursion 150 feet deeper than the saturation exposure. This is the maximum permitted by the 200 and 240 minute half-time limits. We can slide the bar diagram to the left until the increase of helium tension in a faster tissue intersects with its respective M value line.

The depth at which that occurs is the shallow limit for that excursion as a no-decompression dive. In his case both the 20-minute and the 40-minute limits become controlling at about 300 feet saturation depth.

Similar analysis showed limits about 50 and 100 feet lower for the 125/75 and 100/100 excursions. The bar diagram at the left shows the increase in helium tension in all tissues during the 100 feet for 60-minute excursion of Table IV. The shallow saturation limit for this no-decompression excursion would seem to be 150 feet.

The conservative adequacy and safety of the excursion tables and their shallow saturation depth limits have been proved in the test program I referred to. As a matter of fact that they were so raises the consideration that the limits are too conservative and could be safely raised. The graph of Figure 3 was made from the M values of Workman's 1965 report without change. Figure 4 shows a symmetrical adjustment of the M value lines and also a slight slope in the 200 minute M value limit. These limits have not been tested.

The regraphing makes no change in the 20 minute M value line, which was the limiting tissue for the shallow saturation depth of both

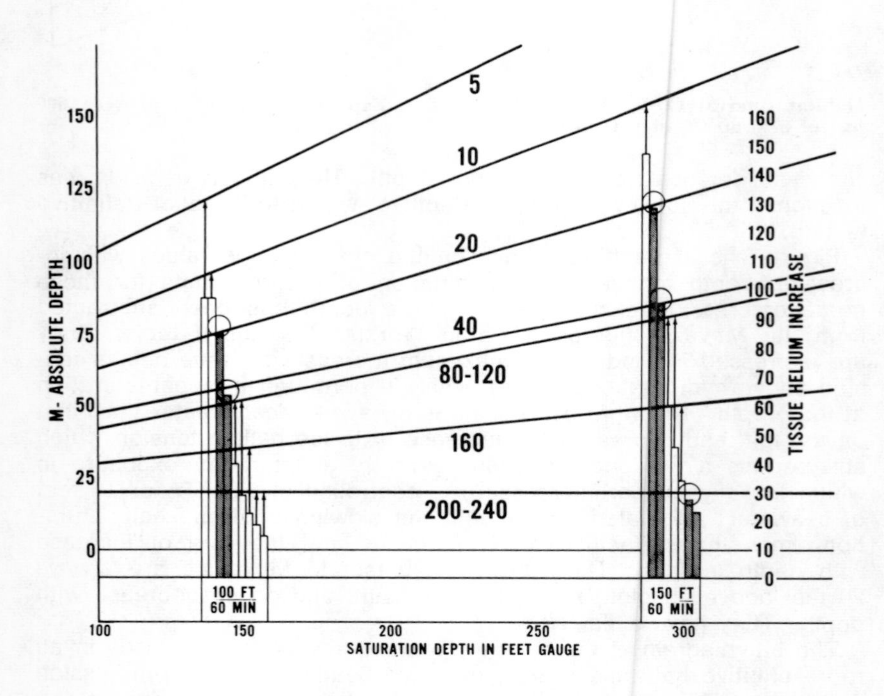

Figure 3: **Increase of Helium tension in representative half-time tissues during two specific excursions plotted against M value limits to determine the shallowest saturation exposure from which these dives would still be no-decompression excursions.**

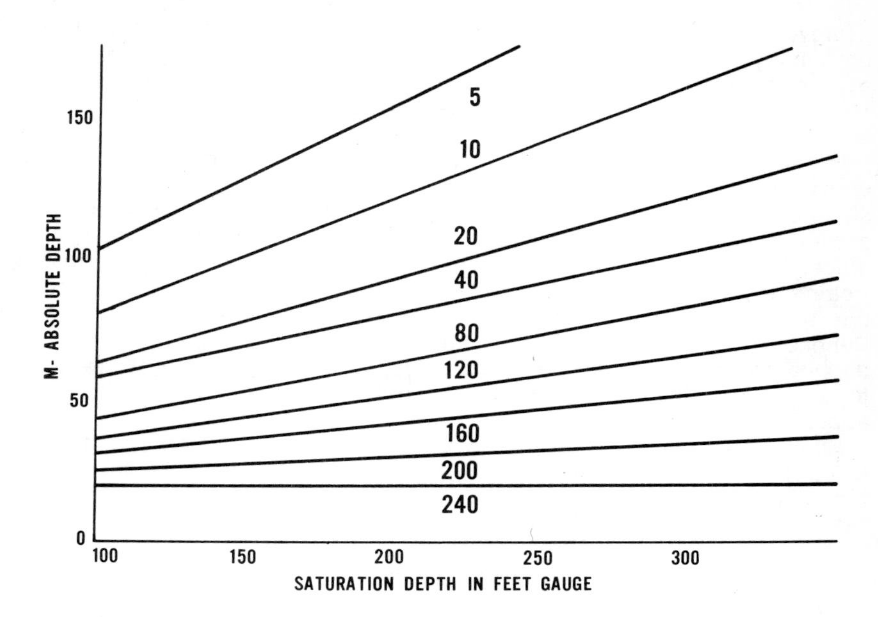

Figure 4: **Speculative symmetrical re-plotting of M value increases with increasing saturation depth. Compare Figure 6.**

Table IV and Table V. However, the slight increase in the 200 minute M value, the small slope, raises the possibility that one hour no-decompression excursions may be possible 250 feet deeper than a saturation exposure as shallow as 600 feet, and an hour excursion 400 feet deeper may be possible from a saturation exposure at 1000 feet.

We can go on as we have been, daring and testing. We have been quite successful in doing so. But it would help enormously if we knew why. The problem is to explain in physical terms why such an increase in permissible dives is possible as the depth becomes greater. We have seen it in short excursions and in decompression from long saturation exposures. One must consider nascent bubbles or "silent" bubbles if he uses supersaturation techniques in decompression. It could be then a question of probability whether a beginning bubble will dissolve or become stable. Most of our studies indicate that the diver's physiologic processes operate normally in the habitat despite any increase in depth. Is there any reason why the critical size of a bubble, the size it must attain to persist, should alter in the body as depth increases?

The molecular volume of inert gas which dissolves is constant per unit increase of depth. The number of molecular coming out of solution per unit of ascent is the same. But if the critical ratio or volume remains the same, the number of molecules necessary to achieve the critical volume increases as the depth increases. The probability that the number of molecules needed are actually available at a critical moment should decrease as the number required increases. The probability for a stable and persistent bubble should increase as depth decreases.

It has been reported that decompression sickness occurring under pressure seems to be easier to treat generally than bends on the surface. Is this related? Is it real? Is it just early treatment, since a subject under continuous observation in a chamber, with a medical officer right there to begin treatment, might well get more rapid treatment as soon as he reports a symptom? In contrast a diver on the surface is a free agent and generally a retreating one. Dr. Behnke reported (1) a consistent interval of 5 to 6 hours to treatment, despite careful instruction that his caisson workers are to go directly to a specific place for treatment immediately after bends symptoms appear.

What is needed? More information about the physical behavior of bubbles in body fluids under diving conditions. And more information about the nature and timing of the pathophysiologic reactions set in train by bubbles in the body.

REFERENCES

[1] Behnke, A. R., "Medical Aspects of Pressurized Tunnel Operations", 1970, in press.
[2] Bornmann, R. C., "Decompression after Saturation Diving", PROCEEDINGS of the Third Symposium on Underwater Physiology, C. J. Lambertsen, ed, Williams & Wilkins, Baltimore, 1967.
[3] Bornmann, R. C., "Decompression Tables for Helium-Oxygen Saturation-Excursion Diving", Research Report 1-70, Deep Submergence Systems Project Office, Chevy Chase, Maryland, in press.
[4] Admiralty Report on Deep-Water Diving, His Majesty's Stationery Office, London, England, 1907.
[5] Hemmingsen, E. A., "Supersaturation of Gases in Water", Science, Vol. 167, pp. 1493-4, 13 March 1970.
[6] Jones, H. B., "Respiratory System Nitrogen Elimination", in Medical Physics, Vol. Two, O. Glaser, ed, Year Book Publishers, Chicago, 1950.
[7] Workman, R. D., "Calculation of Decompression Schedules for Nitrogen-Oxygen and Helium-Oxygen Dives", Research Report 6-65, Experimental Diving Unit, Washington, D. C. 26, May 1965.

REACTION 2
Second Session

Lt. CDR. Mark E. Bradley, MC, USN[1]
Submarine Development Group One
San Diego, Calif.

The Interaction of Stresses in Diving and Adaptation to these Stresses

The physiological stresses encountered in deep diving can be extreme. These same stresses are encountered during dives to 50 or 100 feet, but at these depths they are usually less severe. By reviewing the problems of a specific deep dive the stresses of everyday diving can be illustrated. Moreover, the adaptive processes that a diver can undergo which will modify his responses to these stresses can be examined.

In 1969, U.S. Navy divers made a number of 600 foot open sea dives to evaluate the Mark II Deep Diving System. The Mark II Deep Diving System is designed to support conventional and saturation diving at depths to 850 feet. This diving system comprises two Deck Decompression Chambers with associated life support equipment, and two Personnel Transfer Capsules to transport the divers between the DDC's and the ocean floor.

The first deep dive which was made with the Mark II diving system was extremely stressful. Before, during and after the dive the divers complained bitterly of the cold in the Personnel Transfer Capsule, pressurized to 600 feet with helium-oxygen. One diver stated that the Personnel Transfer Capsule was so cold that his impression on entering 47° F water at 600 feet was that he was stepping into a tepid bath. In the water the divers experienced difficulty with their semi-closer underwater breathing equipment. They stated that breathing with this equipment" was like breathing through a straw — it gave no satisfaction". The dive was terminated after the divers had been in the water about 15 minutes because of cold and the difficulty with the underwater breathing apparatus.

From the tenor of the diver's complaints it was apparent that they had encountered severe physiological stresses. They had been cold,

[1] Opinions and conclusions contained in this paper are those of the author. They are not to be construed as necessarily reflecting the views or the endorsement of the Navy Department.

had become short of breath while using their underwater breathing equipment, and certainly had experienced some psychological stress. The first part of this paper will consider in detail the nature of these stresses and determine to what degree they interacted.

PHYSIOLOGICAL RESPONSES TO STRESS

Cold

The divers were conscious of the cold as soon as they entered the Personnel Transfer Capsule which was pressurized with helium-oxygen to 600 feet. The mean ambient temperature of the PTC for the 3 hours required to make the dive to and from the ocean floor was about 50° F. The divers were dressed in unheated 3/16" foam neoprene suits which were helium equilibrated and compressed to about one half of their original thickness.

Tauber, et al[18]* have calculated that approximately 1000 watts of heat replacement must be provided to keep a diver in thermal balance under these conditions. At sea level pressure in air, the ambient temperature would have to be less than−30° F for a diver to require this amount of heat replacement.

During exposure to low environmental temperatures, special mechanisms are set into play which help to maintain homeostasis. One of the first effects of cold exposure is intense vasoconstriction of the skin vessels over the entire body.[7] This vasoconstriction reduces heat transfer from the internal portions of the body to the periphery. The result is that the insulative layer of the body is effectively increased. Peripheral temperature falls and skin temperatures may approach the ambient temperature. The mean skin temperatures of the divers in the PTC seem to have fallen to levels where 47° F water did not feel cold.

The divers reported that they were violently shivering during their entire stay in the Personnel Transfer Capsule. Shivering is the body's prime means of thermogenesis by which falls in deep body temperature are limited. The metabolic cost of this thermogenesis are increases in the diver's oxygen consumption, carbon dioxide production and ventilation.

A 15 minute exposure to an ambient temperature of 27° F will increase the oxygen consumption of unclothed men to more than 0.8 L/min.[8] Resting oxygen uptakes of 1.7 L/min have been reported in subjects immersed in 61° F water for 20 minutes.[15] The divers in the Personnel Transfer Capsule probably had resting oxygen consumptions of at least 1.5 L/min which resulted from their cold exposure.

Respiration

The work involved in breathing is normally a small fraction of the total energy turnover of normal individuals. However, high ventilations (and moderate ventilations where respiratory impedance is either

---

* refers to numbered bibliography at end of the paper.

intrinsically or extrinsically increased) may require significant amounts of work. During all SCUBA diving, and especially during the dive being discussed, a combination of factors were interacting which increased the oxygen cost of breathing.

Inhalation of air at −20° F doubles inspiratory resistance and to a lesser degree increases expiratory resistance.[(6)] Venous congestion and increased mucus production of the upper airways and possibly some degree of localized bronchospasm are thought to account for these changes. Inhalation of helium — oxygen mixtures which are at higher temperatures but which have a much higher rate of heat transfer may produce similar physiological responses.

The density of helium — oxygen at 19.2 ATA is almost four times that of air at sea level. Breathing a gas mixture of this density will approximately double the diver's airway resistance.[(12)] The work of breathing 30 L/min. of this gas requires about 100 cc/min of additional oxygen by the body. The oxygen consumption of a diver respiring 55 L/min. of helium-oxygen at 600 feet will be increased about 250 cc/min.[(3)]

Breathing with SCUBA increases a diver's respiratory impedance and work of breathing in a number of ways. The first set of factors that adds to work of breathing is the resistance to gas flow of the components of the underwater breathing apparatus and the elasticity of the breathing bags. Any system of check and pop-off valves, corrugated rubber tubing, connectors and carbon dioxide absorbent increases flow resistance. Increased gas density will further increase the flow resistive work of breathing with an underwater breathing apparatus.

Cooper[(5)] has determined the amount of work done against elastic resistance in subjects breathing with a closed-circuit underwater breathing apparatus. He concluded the work done against the elastic forces of this equipment was negligible when compared to the frictional work. However, the compliance of the rubberized breathing bags of underwater breathing equipment will be less in cold water. In this situation there may be a significant increase in the work required to overcome the elastic characteristics of the equipment.

The second factor that increases work of breathing with an underwater breathing apparatus results from imbalances of hydrostatic pressure acting upon the diver's lungs and the breathing bags or demand valve of his equipment. The most common positions that a SCUBA diver assumes in the water are the upright (vertical) position and the prone (swimming) position. With the exhaust valve of their underwater breathing apparatus 1/3 closed, the Mark II Diving System divers were positive pressure breathing at +15 cm of H_2O in the swimming position. In the vertical position they were negative pressure breathing at −10 cm of H_2O.[(13)]

Both positive and negative pressure breathing impair nervous coordination of respiratory musculature and shift intrapulmonary pressure — volume relationships. The result is that the diver breathes less efficiently and work of breathing increases. There is considerable evidence which indicates that a diver's work of breathing is not considerably altered by positive pressure breathing if the diver is able to adapt and accept shifts of his intrapulmonary pressures and volumes.[17]

Negative pressure breathing at −10 cm of H_2O decreases lung volume and causes compression of the extrathoracic airways.[1] As a consequence the diver's airway resistance is almost doubled and this, coupled with the shifts in breathing to less efficient areas, may cause significant increases in work of breathing.

Psychological Stress

Psychological as well as cold stress causes stimulation of the sympathetic nervous system with liberation of norepinephrine and epinephrine. These hormones have a direct effect on cells to cause glycogenolysis. This, probably along with other intracellular effects of these hormones, increases cellular activity and the metabolic rate of essentially all the tissues of the body.

Interactions

During the dive with the Mark II Deep Diving System, the thermal, respiratory and psychological stresses which were experienced each had its own unique set of consequences. However, one physiological response that each of these stresses produced was an increase in the diver's oxygen uptake. (Fig. 1)

The maximum oxygen consumption that can be attained with the underwater breathing apparatus that these divers were using is about 3.0 L/min.[2] Above this level any oxygen additionally gained would be required for the work of breathing. By the interaction of thermal, respiratory and psychological stresses the divers had oxygen consumptions at rest which were probably in excess of 2.0 L/min. The light exercise then required to perform underwater tasks further increased the diver's oxygen uptake. The result was that the maximum oxygen consumption permitted during use of this underwater breathing apparatus was attained. At this point the divers found that breathing with their equipment no longer satisfied their oxygen needs and they became short of breath.

ADAPTATION

For one reason or another, one diver is better able to cope with a given stress than another diver. This can be termed natural resistance. All conditions which disturb the normal functioning of an individual lead to defense reactions which attempts to maintain constant the conditions of life in the internal environment. By means of adaptation the original responses to stress can be modified so that a more economical and broader homeostasis results which reduces the strain of the body and mind. Adaptation to psychological stress is the domain of the experimental psychologist and will not be discussed in this paper.

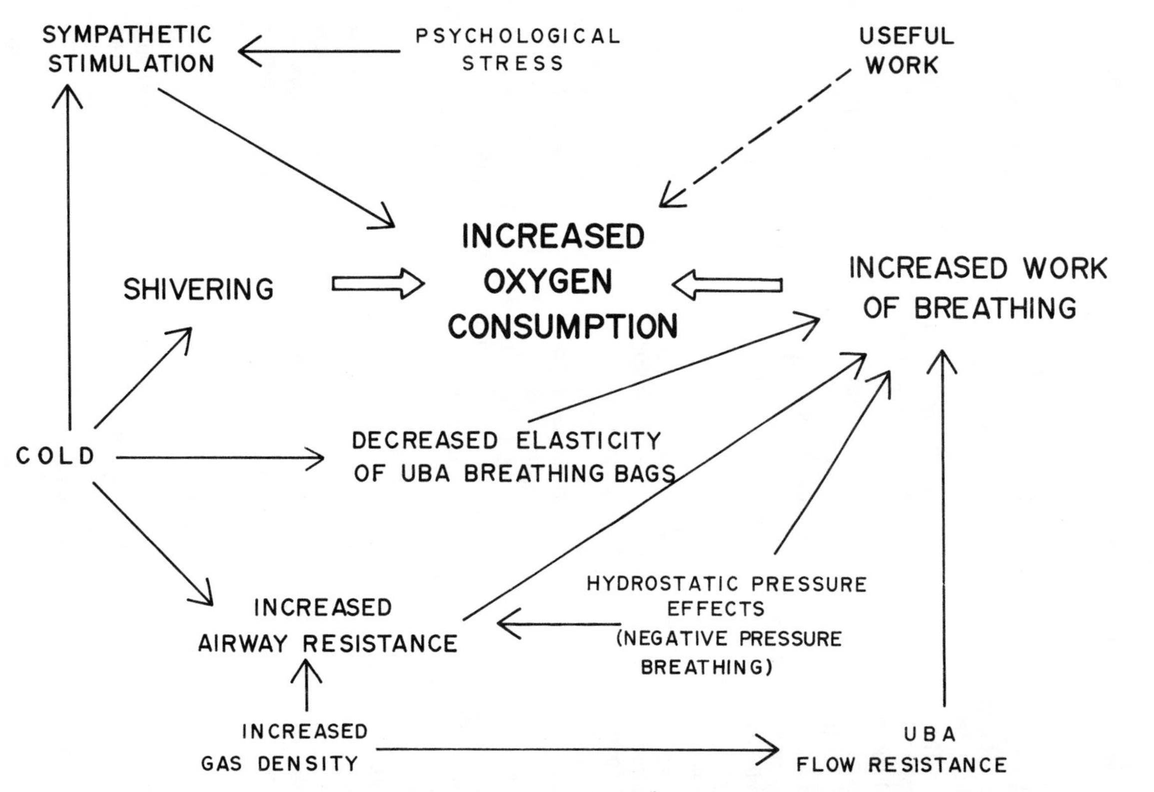

Figure 1: **The interaction of factors which increased the Mark 11 Diving System diver's oxygen consumption.**

Cold

Fat effectively insulates against cold. Channel swimmers who endure long periods in cold water have been shown to possess unusually thick layers of subcutaneous fat.[15] Keatings[10] contended that individuals whose mean subcutaneous fat is less than 10 mm thick are basically unsuitable for work in cold water, while those with subcutaneous fat more than 20 mm thick are highly suitable. Thus, the primary long-term action that a diver can take to improve his physiological ability to maintain thermal balance in cold water is to increase his subcutaneous fat.

Habituation to cold environments can cause marked changes in the human responses to cold. Adapted divers tolerate cold water with less discomfort and shivering and sustain smaller drops in deep body temperature during cold exposures than those who are not acclimatized.[16] In the acclimatized state there is a reduced metabolic response to cold so that metabolic energy is conserved.[11] This acquired acclimatization appears to be a labile mechanism which dissipates in two weeks after cold exposures are discontinued.

Respiration

Intrinsic and extrinsic increases in gas flow resistance are the largest source of increased work of breathing in SCUBA diving. Divers adapt to respiring against added frictional resistance by altering their breathing pattern. It can be theoretically predicted that when flow resistance is increased, the optimal respiratory frequency becomes lower in order to minimize the energy expenditure required for breathing.[14] In subjects breathing against imposed resistance[4] and in divers breathing dense gas mixtures,[3] respiratory frequency is decreased and mean tidal volume is increased.

During exercise many divers hypoventilate and retain carbon dioxide. Breathing against external resistance and breathing dense gas accentuates the hypoventilation and hypercapnia.[9] Why a diver's ventilatory response to exertion is inadequate, whereas an inexperienced or non-diver's is "normal" is not clear at this time. This phenomenon may represent an adaptive mechanism which the diver employs in preference to spending the extra energy required to maintain ventilation at an optimal level.

CONCLUSIONS

At shallow depths a diver may be subjected to stresses which are qualitatively similar to those ecountered during deep diving. In deep diving and in certain types of shallow diving, these stresses can be severe and can interact to endanger the diver and degrade his capacity for physical exertion.

Avoidance or minimizing the effects of these stresses enhances diver productivity and safety. Proper diver selection and training will improve a diver's ability to cope with the rigors of diving. The equipment that a diver uses must support his physiologically. His thermal balance must be maintained by a thick, well fitting wet suit or by providing supplemental heat. The underwater breathing apparatus that a diver uses should incorporate characteristics of low flow resistance, minimal dead space and minimal hydrostatic imbalance in order to lessen work of breathing.

REFERENCES

[1] Agostoni, E., G. Gurtner, G. Torri and H. Rahn: *Respiratory Mechanics During Submersion and Negative Pressure Breathing.* J. Appl. Physiol. 21 (1):251-258, 1966.

[2] Anthonisen, N. R.: *Physiological Studies of the Mark IX Mixed Gas SCUBA.* Naval Medical Research Institute Project M4306.7-1003, Research Rpt. No. 1, 1969.

[3] Bradley, M. E., J. Vorosmarti, N. R. Anthonisen and P. G. Linaweaver: *Respiratory and Cardiac Responses to Exercise While Breathing HeO_2 from Sea Level to 19.2 Atmospheres.* in Proc. 4th Sympos. on Underwater Physiol. (in press).

[4] Cain, C. C. and A. B. Otis: *Some Physiologic Effects Resulting From Added Resistance to Respiration.* J. Aviation Med., Vol. 20:149, 1949.

[5] Cooper, E. A.: *Suggested Methods of Testing And Standards of Resistance for Protective Devices.* J. Appl. Physiol. 15 (6):1053-1061, 1960.

[6] Guleria, J. S., J. R. Talwar, O. P. Mahotra and J. N. Pande: *Effect of Breathing Cold Air on Pulmonary Mechanics in Normal Man.* J. Appl. Physiol. 27 (3): 320-322, 1969.

[7] Hardy, J. D.: *Physiology of Temperature Regulation.* Physiol. Rev. 41:521-606, 1961.

[8] Horvath, S. M., G. B. Spurr, B. K. Hutt and L. H. Hamilton: *Metabolic Cost of Shivering. J. Appl.* Physiol. 8:595-602, 1956.

[9] Lanphier, E. H.: *Influence of Increased Ambient Pressure Upon Alveolar Ventilation.* in: Proceedings of the Second Underwater Physiology Symposium. Natl. Acad. Sci., Natl. Res. Council Publ. 1181, Wash., D.C., 1963, pp. 124-133.

[10] Keatinge, W. R.: *Survival in Cold Water.* Oxford, Blackwell Scientific Publications, 1969.

[11] Leblanc, J.: *Adaptive Mechanisms in Humans.* Ann. N.Y. Acad. Sci. 134 (2):721-732, 1966.

[12] Marshall, R., E. H. Lanphier and A. B. Dubois: *Resistance to Breathing in Normal Subjects During Simulated Dives.* J. Appl. Physiol. 9:5-10, 1956.

[13] O'Neill, W. J.: *A Study of the Breathing Hydrostatics of Various Bag-Type Diving Apparatuses and Description of the Two Valve Toroidal and Abalone Backmounted Design.* Westinghouse Ocean Res. And Elgin. Center Res. Rpt., 1969.

[14] Otis, A. M.: *The Work of Breathing.* Handbook of Physiol., Respiration, Vol. I, ed. W. O. Fenn and H. Rahn, Wash., D. C., Amer. Physiol. Coc., 1965, Chap. 17.

[15] Pugh, L. G. C. E.: *Temperature Regulation in Swimmers.* in Physiology of Breath-Hold Diving and The AMA Of Japan, Natl. Res. Coun. Publ. 1341, Wash., D. C., 1965.

[16] Skreslet, S. and F. Aarejoro: *Acclimatization to Cold in Man Induced by Frequent SCUBA Diving in Cold Water.* J. Appl. Physiol. 24 (2):177-181, 1968.

[17] Submarine Medicine Practice (NavMed P-5054). Washington, D.C., Govn. Print. Off., 1956.

[18] Tauber, J. F., J. S. P. Rawlins and K. R. Bondi: *Theoretical Thermal Requirements For the Mark II Diving System.* Naval Medical Research Institute Project M4306.02-6010B, Res. Rpt. No. 2, 1969.

REACTION 3
Second Session

Compression Arthralgia and Aseptic Bone Necrosis in Divers

CDR James Vorosmarti, Jr., MC, USN[1]
Submarine Development Group One
San Diego, Calif.

The first report of an episode of what is now referred to as compression arthralgia was made by Case and Haldane in 1941.[(1)]* These investigators described the loud cracking sounds produced by Haldane's shoulders during a 320 foot dive. The syndrome of compression arthralgia is a collection of vague joint symptoms which occur during compression to higher than atmospheric pressure. The complaints range from mild popping or cracking of joints to frank pain on motion. There is an associated sensation variously described as "no joint juice",[(2)] "joints not meshing properly", and "mild sprain". In no instance is there involvement of the soft tissue surrounding the joint, such as swelling or inflammation. Because of the deeper depths now attainable through saturation diving techniques a larger percentage of divers have been experiencing these symptoms. During the saturation dives conducted in preparation for Sealab III, the concern over the high incidence of this syndrome was responsible for the decrease in compression rate from 60 ft/min. to 40 ft/hr.

There were two basic reasons for this change. The first was the discomfort caused the diver. Although no cases have been severe enough to prevent a diver from accomplishing a job, the addition of an aggravating problem to an already uncomfortable and stressful situation is definitely detrimental. The second and more important reason for slowing the compression rate was concern that this syndrome signaled the occurrence of tissue injury. If this was so, this area of trauma could be a focus for bubble formation and decompression sickness. The Medical Department of Submarine Development Group ONE is conducting a retrospective study of saturation dives in order to further elucidate the syndrome of compression arthralgia. This presentation concerns some preliminary information gained from ques-

[1] Opinions and conclusions contained in this report are those of the author. They are not to be construed as necessarily reflecting the views or the endorsement of the Navy Department.

* Refers to numbered bibliography at end of paper.

tioning 58 divers representing 104 man-dives. These divers were subjects on dives ranging from 100 feet to 1000 feet in depth and were exposed to compression rates of from 60 ft/min. to 40 ft/hr.

One general observation that has been made is that there is a considerable inter- and intra-individual variation in this syndrome. A diver may have symptoms on one dive and none on the next dive. Some divers never experience arthralgia, while others always have symptoms. One joint may be affected in one dive, and yet different joints may be painful at another time.

The overall incidence of pain occurring in the divers surveyed was 43%. This figure is not very meaningful in itself but if the incidence of pain is compared to the depth of the dive one sees what appears to be a dose response relationship (Fig. 1). If one correlates the incidence of pain according to depth and either the fast (40-60 ft/min.) or slow (40 ft/hr.) compression rate the relationship is still present (Table 1). These figures indicate that using the slower rate of compression does not prevent compression arthralgia but the incidence is decreased for specific depths. The data on the severity of pain have been analyzed incompletely but it appears that the slower rate of compression also decreases the severity of the pain. Table 1 also indicates that depth is a much more important factor than is the compression rate.

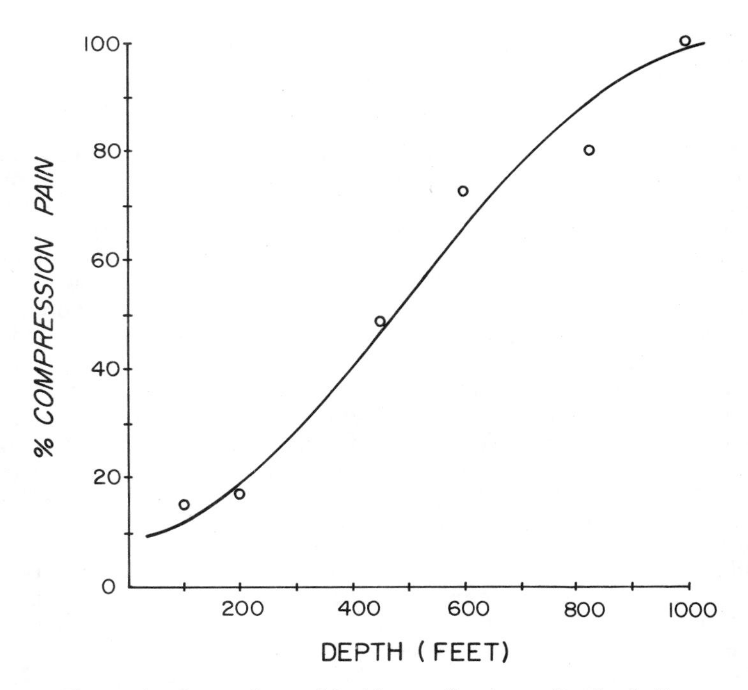

Figure 1: **Comparison of incidence of pain to depth of dive.**

TABLE 1

THE INCIDENCE OF PAIN ACCORDING TO DIVE DEPTH AND COMPRESSION RATE

DEPTH	FAST	SLOW
100	8%	33%
200	16%	--
450	75%	44%
600	100%	68%
825	--	80%
1000	--	100%

Although the incidence of pain is high the severity is very mild. Seventy percent of the divers who experienced compression pains classified them as mild, 28 percent as moderate, while only one man described the pain as severe. The joints most commonly affected were the shoulders and knees, followed by wrists, ankles, hips and elbows. The least affected joints were those of the fingers and toes. In all but a few cases the pain disappeared within 24 hours at depth and the majority of these cleared in 5-10 hours. As stated above these are only preliminary findings and more data will need to be collected and analyzed before any definite conclusions can be drawn.

The rate of compression has gained more importance recently for another reason. Dr. B. A. Hills of Duke University is conducting a retrospective study of caisson workers. He feels that there is a positive correlation between the incidence of aseptic bone necrosis and a fast compression rate. At present, the most probable cause of aseptic bone necrosis is inadequate decompression.

Although it has been known since the early part of this century that caisson workers were susceptible to this disease it was not until 1936 that the first case was reported in a diver (3). There has been an increasing number of cases reported in divers since then (4). It is enough of a potential problem that both the Royal and United States Navies have instituted programs of periodic x-ray screening.

The following cases of aseptic bone necrosis have not previously been reported. The second case is the first to be reported in which a saturation dive has been incriminated as the probable cause. Both of these cases were identified as a result of routine x-ray screening.

CASE 1. J.M. is a 31 year old male who has been actively engaged in diving since 1953 and involved in experimental deep diving since 1963. In January of 1965 he developed decompression sickness involving both knees during a 600 foot non-saturation dive. There was no residual after treatment. He developed bilateral knee bends again in February 1965 during decompression from a 650 foot non-saturation dive. Again no residual was noted after treatment. He has had no symptoms of bone or joint disease. General physical examination and specialized orthopedic examination at the time the x-rays were taken revealed no abnormalities. X-rays of the shoulders, hips and knees were taken on September 1968. No lesions were noted in the knees or left femoral head. Patchy sclerosis interspersed with cystic rarefraction was noted in the right femoral head. Both humeral heads contained posterior-superior subchondral lesions with diffuse osteosclerosis. No evidence of articular surface involvement was noted. No follow-up x-rays are available at the present time.

CASE 2. M.S.C. at the time of the x-ray study was a 43 year old male and former Navy pilot and astronaut. Past history revealed an episode of bilateral elbow pain in 1957 following rapid decompression to 25,000 feet in an aircraft. There was no residual from this episode. He began diving in 1965 and during decompression from a 30-day, 205 foot saturation dive that year experienced progressive anterior thigh pain bilaterally. The thigh pain and quadriceps weakness while climbing stairs persisted for two weeks. He was not treated for decompression sickness at that time. General physical examination and specialized orthopedic examination at the time of the x-ray survey was normal. Roentgenograms were taken of his hips, knees and shoulders on 29 August 1968. These revealed bilateral, poorly calcified, irregular, serpentine metadiaphyseal lesions of the distal femoral shafts. There was no evidence of hip or knee involvement. No lesions were noted in the shoulders. The subject was disqualified for further diving duty at that time. No follow-up x-rays are available at present.

These cases add to an increasing series of aseptic bone necrosis in divers.

REFERENCES

[1] CASE, E. M., HALDANE, J. B. S.: Human Physiology Under High Pressure. I. Effects of Nitrogen, Carbon Dioxide, and Cold. *Jour. Hygiene* 41:225-249, 1941.

[2] HAMILTON, R. W., MACINNIS, J. B., NOBLE, A. D., SCHREINER, H. R.: Saturation Diving at 650 Feet. Ocean Systems Inc., Tech. Memo. B-411,15 MAR 1966.

[3] SEIFERT, Z., Cited in HOFF, E. C.,: A Bibliographical Sourcebook of Compressed Air, Diving and Submarine Medicine, P 158, U. S. Government Printing Office, Washington, D. C., 1948.

[4] UHL, R. R.: Aseptic Bone Necrosis in Divers, *Aerospace Med.* 39: 1345-1347, 1968.

DISCUSSION
Second Session

Dr. Bradner: I think considering the fact that we are running not too far but significantly behind time, I'd like to suggest that we set a goal of ending the public discussion at, let's say, half an hour from now, and that we try to keep the questions now to those things which you felt to be of general interest. Those questions which you'd like to address individually to the panelists, you can get down on the beach and perhaps get longer answers. I'll also do the quite unfair thing of asking the panelists to make as brief answer as they think they can and still have it comprehensible. Were there some of the written questions that you feel are succinct and generally important that should be tackled? Would you like to hit that first?

Lt. Cdr. Bradley: I have one question by Mr. Morgan here which is simply, can we heat breathing gases to 120° to 130° and obtain a usable heat input? My answer to this is that we may have to heat breathing gases for the reason which I've shown. One, because of undesirable physiological effects such as bronchial spasm, increased airway resistance. Now this whole problem of respiratory heat loss in especially helium environments is a real bug-ab-ear. By and large, most of what we know or think is based upon theoretical calculations. Respiratory heat loss can be significant as you probably are aware. It's thought that a diver at 600 feet breathing helium oxygen who has a respiratory minute volume or who was breathing 15 liters a minute will have a respiratory heat loss in the order of 125 watts. If his respiratory minute volume increases to 50 liters a minute, it will be in the order of magnitude of about 600 watts. You take a diver down to a thousand feet with this respiratory minute volume of 50 liters a minute, this'll be around a thousand watts. So, respiratory heat loss in a helium environment can be significant. We could minimize this by providing him with heated air.

Indeed, there's probably going to be the time that it's going to be desirable. But, I don't think that we can provide the diver with all the heat replacement he is going to need simply by giving him heated gas. A diver with warm lungs and cold toes is going to be very, very uncomfortable. You're talking I'd say a thousand feet, in terms of a very, very large amount heat replacement, probably an excess of 2,000 watts and 40° water breathing heliox. Does that answer your question, sir?

Cdr. Bornmann: Hugh, may I make additional comments? A living human body manufactures heat. The problem is not one of replacing it but limiting the loss of heat. We put heat into a suit to make sure he doesn't lose heat from his skin as rapidly as he would in a naked or underprotected condition. I think the same thing goes for heating the breathing gas. You want to heat it so that he doesn't lose too much, but I don't think that it is economical to think of it as a means of getting heat back into his body.

I have another one which is rather difficult to answer. It's from Loch Vetter and I'm not sure whether I can but I'll read it: I've heard of clinical methods to permanently enlarge the Eustachian tubes to facilitate air passage. Could you comment on the value of such procedure for a diver with small tubes who suffer on every dive from altonobaric vertigo?

Medical officers used to be — I'm familiar with the case of medical officers — used to be disqualified from diving because they could not clear their ears on the chamber dive that was premilinary to acceptance in diving school. They used to send them out to Bethesda to have (I think it was radium treatment) radiation treatment to reduce the lymphatic tissue in their nasal pharynx and to facilitate opening of the Eustachian tube. Most doctors, when presented with that alternative, said, "Forget it," and I don't think it's been done for years. Now, there are certain things that can be done. I'd recommend that the individual concerned go see his doctor and find out what his specific problem is and what specific remedies are available. It can be done if you're a trained diver, or if it's something new perhaps it can be remedied. If you're someone who's not a diver who's thinking of going into diving or who's only just begun it, there are a lot of other things that you could find as a hobby that would . . . I'll be frank about it. I certainly wouldn't want my nasal pharynx radiated just to open the Eustachian tube.

Cdr. Vorosmarti: I'd like to make a comment on that and I have a question I'd like to reply to. Also, that, whoever this person is, if he's having vertigo on every dive and can't do anything about it, he ought to quit diving because one of these times he may get into a situation where he can't handle the vertigo. It's not too nice to vomit in your mouhpiece when you're at 60 feet or to lose consciousness. So, I agree, that he ought to pick a safer hobby.

Cdr. Vorosmarti: Here's a question: Discuss the use of drugs in a diver. They specifically talk about aspirin and decongestants. I don't see any problem with aspirin and decongestants. In fact, if you're going to dive and you're having problems clearing your ears, I would suggest using decongestants and I cannot see any problem in taking aspirin before you go diving. We've used decongestants, aspirin, darvon, and a lot of other drugs on saturation runs and haven't run into any problems. It doesn't mean they're safe in all cases. We still don't know how people react differently to drugs under high pressures, if indeed they do. There's some work going on in the field now, but I don't know enough about it to comment on that.

Cdr. Hoke: Jim, I'd like to add, too, that I've had experience one time with a diver who'd made a 100-foot dive. It was a no-decompression dive. After the dive he came up with some parasthesias and numbness of his thights. I was just about to get ready to treat this diver for decompression sickness, neurological symptoms, but then they began shifting. You know, a little bit here and then it's over here, so I waited a few minutes and pretty soon they were clearing up. I got to talking with him and the day before he'd had a backache and someone had given him some muscle relaxants. Before he'd made this dive, about an hour before, he'd taken a dose of a muscle relaxant and one of the side effects of muscle relaxants is to produce this kind of symptoms in some people. So, watch using muscle relaxants. If you've got a backache and your're gonna dive, just dive. Don't louse yourself up with drugs or else don't dive.

Cdr. Vorosmarti: Common treatment for muscular aches and pains, stiff muscles, sore backs, is a combination of muscle relaxants and darvon and this is not a good idea to take before you go diving.

Cdr. Hoke: Because the side effects will mimic. . . .

Cdr. Vorosmarti: Yes, not only will the side effects mimic decompression sickness, but they're also central nervous system decompressants. The combination of both of them will cause quite a loss with your knowledge of what's going on around you, especially if you couple that with a little nitrogen narcosis.

Lt. Cdr. Bradley: Also coupled with a little alcohol.

Dr. Bradner: Are there other remarks on this general question of the drugs?

Audience question: What about antihistamines?

Cdr. Vorosmarti: I think I classify the antihistamines as part of the central nervous system sedative drugs in that case and I don't think anybody ought to be taking amphetimaines unless they need it for a medical reason. Certainly not to stay awake so you can make a dive.

Dr. Bradner: Question in the next to the last row.

Audience question: Inaudible.

Cdr. Hoke: I'll comment on that. That was done by the people at Virginia Mason, I believe, and they were aerosolyzing drugs and having guinea pigs breathe them, either in, aerosolyzed in oxygen or aerosolyzed in air and they were aerosolyzing things like theophel and hemanopheline, but as a control they also aerosolyzed some water and another set of guinea pigs on oxygen. They saw no difference in the therapeutic outcome in the guinea pigs that had aerosolyzed water and those that had aerosolyzed diaphra which is a bronchial dilator and so they've really not pursued the studies after that. They thought they were on to something good until they discovered that their controls had an equally successful run from the . . .

There was a difference between the ones that had water and they didn't get it at all, but the fact that the nebulized water itself was therapeutic, as I said, caused them to feel like they were dealing with one of the mysteries of life.

Cdr. Bornmann: The primary discipline against decompression sickness is adequate recompression. Now, sometimes you get it. The only therapy, the only adequate therapy for decompression sickness is decompression. Without that you have inadequate therapy. With it, it is sometimes adequate by itself. Nothing more needs to be done. However, sometimes also even recompression is not sufficient and these other drugs and everything the doctor can do to assist the patient under those conditions should be done. It's a test of his medical skill and art. I want to emphasize that the treatment of decompression sickness is recompression. Without that, treatment is inadequate.

Cdr. Hoke: Not the occupation to be in if you have to have a drug. . . .

Audience Question: How about lung flooding?

Cdr. Hoke: Mark, why don't you take on lung flooding?

Cdr. Bradley: Well, let's deal with lung flooding first. Better your lungs than mine. I really think this is a good way off as yet. When you start talking about liquid breathing, there's unfortunately one real problem with it. You can get oxygen in but you can't get CO_2 out very well. And, often you have a bit of a trouble even getting the O_2 in. You talk in terms of power resisted respiration of this fluid. You are breathing soup and it requires a lot of work, like it's something about 40 times the normal work of breathing. Well, can you empower assist respiration then? Well, possibly you can but really I think this is well in the future. I'm sure it can be traumatic psychologically, too, and I just don't think the state of the art is here yet.

Now in regard to rehydration and some of the work that Cockett has done showing that dehydrated experimental animals have a much higher susceptibility to recompression sickness than animals which are well hydrated. I think it would be very, very pleasant or very good if we could effectively moisturize the gas the diver is breathing. Subjectively, he would be much more comfortable. Unfortunately, what we're once again faced with is a technical engineering problem and that anything you put in there is probably going to require a power source from some place. If it's a diver's lungs or something of this nature, then you have yet another source of increased work of breathing. Yes, moisturized air is good. But at the moment, it doesn't appear too feasible.

Cdr. Bornmann: There's another technical problem in that some of the semi-closed apparatus. You're using an orifice which causes supersonic gas flow and if gas is highly saturated, you might run into problems of the orifice freezing.

Lt. Cdr. Bradley: If that happens, you ain't got no gas.

Dr. Bradner: I think you had a question a moment ago.

Cdr. Hoke (in answer to inaudible audience question): Well, some research was undertaken about two years ago at Bethesda in a project to do hyperbaric pharmacology in which several drugs were tested on animals at depths up to 600 feet. They tried epinephrine and cortisone and aspirin and a sleeping pill of some kind and something else — I can't remember the fifth one — and they determined no distinct pharmacologic difference as in the action of the drugs at 600 feet in mice. That's right, I know, that's why I mentioned that it was in mice because you know that, but if you know what the effect is in the mouse at one atmosphere, and you take him to 20 atmospheres and you don't see any different effects, then you get a pretty good idea that in the mouse it's safe. You may think it's safe in a human. But you've got to do it to find out and that's what you're really saying.

Lt. Cdr. Bradley: This is a sorely needed area of research and one which. . . .

I agree with you. It's preferable not to take any drugs. Unfortunately, in actual situation you will find at times when you do have to prescribe drugs for divers and there is an inherent risk in this.

Cdr. Bornmann (in answer to inaudible question): That happened to an instructor at the training tank except that he wasn't in a chamber.

He was in a blister about half-way down. He'd gotten a sinus squeeze and he went down to relieve it. Then he couldn't get back up again and he was struck just in a small blister. He finally got up, but he was losing a little bit of blood. He knocked off diving when he had a cold which he should have done before.

Audience question: Any one would think that someone that had had a dislocated hip or dislocated shoulder due to an accident would be more inclined to get an air bubble or a decompression problem in that joint that had been damaged previously?

Cdr. Hoke: I think we have difference of opinion on the panel. I'd like to say that I think he will. In a person that's had an injury, experience and increased likelihood of getting muscular skeletal decompression sickness — but there's some disagreement on the point. Mark, you said you disagreed with that point.

Lt. Cdr. Bradley: I agree with Dr. Hoke theoretically. Unfortunately. when you start looking around at all the divers in the U. S. Navy who have sustained some rather serious accidents, fractures, dislocations, and so forth and so on, whether by motorcycles or falls of a curb or something of this sort, in the vast majority of cases you don't find that there is an increase in decompression sickness in that particular joint. There are instances, believe me, but I'm speaking in terms, in generalities. Perhaps Dr. Bornmann or Capt. Behnke would care to comment on that.

Capt. Behnke: Well, I think if you take this individual up two altitudes and the nitrogen, and the body is saturated, so to speak, then one gets into the trouble. The reason a diver does not have as much trouble, they're . . . but I think the saturation divers have. I'd like to make one more remark. Vertigo and dizziness, I think, are used rather loosely, in a sense. Now, vertigo is a very serious condition that involves the vestibular nerve and sometimes it is necessary to go down to depths of 450 feet. Now, that's really serious. Dizziness — a lot of us are dizzy in our old age.

Cdr. Vorosmarti: Dr. Bradley and I just published a report on altonobaric vertigo on a series that we did. It's very difficult when you're talking to a diver or reading a questionnaire to decide whether the man really had vertigo or whether he was dizzy for some other reason.

Capt. Behnke: Define vertigo . . . just so we understand it.

Cdr. Bradley: Vertigo is a subjective sensation in which either you or your environment is spinning around each other.

Capt. Behnke: . . . way you're going. Isn't that right, dizziness?

Cdr. Bradley: That's one of the definitions, but a lot of people call dizziness the feeling they're going to faint or they're going to black out or something like this. This isn't vertigo. Vertigo is a definite . . .

Dr. Bradner: Twirling.

Capt. Behnke: It's what I call spinning dizziness, to make the distinction.

Lt. Cdr. Bradley: And it's very uncomfortable. Dizziness a lot of times isn't uncomfortable at all, but vertigo can be a very anxiety arousing problem.

Dr. Bradner: I think we have time for about two more questions.

Audience question: I was wondering if there's any physiological evidence about vertisinia — as far as the slowing down — and is there any actual evidence about how it affects the diver in the water?

Cdr. Hoke: No, that's, the reason that it hasn't been done is because the diver doesn't just go underwater and sit there. He goes down underwater for a task and, so, while he's there, he's working. The only evidence I've seen is some that Glen Egstrom has in which he shows that the sort of a task that a diver has that would normally increase his heart rate to about 160 or 170 at one atmosphere. He's seen the same sort of task done underwater with peak heart rates of only around 140 and 150. I suspect it may be partly, Glen, due to this phenomenon of abradiocardia pressure. But it's just a feeling I have; I don't have any physiological background.

Audience question: Inaudible.

Cdr. Bornmann: I'm not sure what you're referring to. The new diving manual came out last week and it had in it standard air tables that I handed out in limited supply.

They're still the same ones that were put together in 1956. Now, the Bureau of Medicine Surgery had new helium oxygen deep-sea diving tables computed. They have not been tested. I don't know how to explain the situation, but the old ones are inadequate for the longer, deeper dives. However, no bureaucrat, no naval officer in a bureau is going to take them out of the manual simply because someone says they're inadequate. They've been there for 25 years. So, what do you do with the poor diving operator? He's got a job he has to get done. The diving tables will at least get him close to the surface where he gets decompression sickness. We have doctors to take care of that. You can't just cut him off. But he means to do his job. I hope to get these things tested sufficiently to replace them.

Now, the changes. I haven't gone into computation of the old table. Dr. Behnke might be able to help me a little more on this. I understand that they were calculated for twice the bottom time but that they only took into account shorter halftime. All the experience we've had since then is that you have to take into account longer half-times which will give you a requirement for more decompression close to the surface and that will be essentially the difference between them when they are tested so that we can publish them. You'll have a longer decompression between 50 feet and the surface. Since that's mostly oxygen, you get into the secondary problem of how much oxygen can you stand for repeated diving exposures. Until we solve that problem, we're not going to be able to come up with a schedule or a table of schedules that's going ot be of much use to the operator.

Dr. Bradner: I think that we've hit the hour of adjournment. Those of you who would like to continue the discussion, I'm sure will find these people are receptive. Tomorrow morning at 9 o'clock, again here. Meanwhile things are starting down on the beach anytime you wish to go there.

Diver Work Method
Third Session

Speaker: **Dr. Gershon Weltman**
Biotechnology Laboratory
School of Engineering and Applied Science
UCLA

Panelists: **Dr. W. S. Vaughan, Jr., President**
Oceanantics, Inc.
Alexandria, Virginia

Dr. Hugh A. Bowen
Managing Scientist
Dunlap & Association, Inc.
Darien, Connecticut

John T. Quirk
U. S. Navy Civil Engineering Laboratory
Port Hueneme, California

Chairman: **Dr. Hugh Bradner**
Scripps Institution of Oceanography
La Jolla, California

Diver Work Methods

Gershon Weltman, Ph.D.
Biotechnology Laboratory
School of Engineering and Applied Science
UCLA

INTRODUCTION

The deep sea diver generally performs quite commonplace work. Jobs such as pipeline inspection, using hand tools to put together or take apart various structures, welding, etc. are no more than are expected of most mechanics or technicians. It is the underwater environment which transforms the divers' task to a highly skilled occupation. Only the astronauts work in a stranger, more risky locale — and theirs is a part-time job, done for satisfactions other than wages. Moreover, the astronaut has behind him virtually all the resources of our modern technology. In many instances diving technology, reflected in the type of equipment which the diver wears, breaths from and uses as tools, is just now beginning to change after remaining essentially the same for about 75 years.

To operate successfully the diver must take into account the various effects of the water around him, and utilize a number of special skills. In accomplishing a typical underwater job, the diver's motor activities range from fine manipulation to man-handling of heavy weights. His body location and orientation change constantly. Submerged objects and tools must be located and identified. Problems imposed by the task and environment must be recognized and solved. Finally, the diver must coordinate his actions with his partner and frequently with a topside station, generally without adequate communication facilities.

We cannot in this paper treat all aspects of the diver's complicated work methodology. In fact, not all aspects are presently known, as we will point out in the conclusions. What we can do is discuss in brief some of the major factors which influence the diver's ability to do work, and in addition, discuss the ways in which diving work is observed in the laboratory under controlled ocean conditions, and on the job. The factors we have concentrated on might be termed the "extrabaric" ones; that is, those effects related more to the watery surroundings than to pressure or depth. We have included a good deal about experimental technique because this in itself is an important factor in diving research. The same effects which make life hard for the diver also make it hard for the diving investigator. Several recent publications have described the use and development of diving test batteries composed of a number of separate measurements, which relate to individual activities or skills (Baddeley et al, 1968; Reilly and Cameron. 1968; Bowen, 1968). Studies adapting this approach are of great value in clarifying the specific effects of underwater environments, but it is frequently difficult to integrate their results to form a picture of performance on "real" underwater jobs. At UCLA, underwater performance research has emphasized the use of comprehensive task simulations which incorporate virtually the full range of diving skills.

Since our interest is in work measurement methodology, as well as diver performance itself, this approach has had the double advantage of providing both a framework within which field measurement techniques can be developed and data on divers closely related to real-life performance. The first steps in this research were undertaken in 1967, when a simulated construction task was developed with a set of techniques for procedural and physiological underwater work measurement (Weltman et al, 1968). This task, called the "pipe puzzle," has been used in a number of studies. During the summer of 1968, the UCLA group participated in the shallow water trials of the Sealab III Divercom project. This gave us an excellent chance to observe professional divers at work on a long, hard, and quite complicated job. The present paper emphasizes the UCLA studies, but also includes the work of other investigators in this small, but intensely active field.

FACTORS INFLUENCING DIVER WORK

Strength and Mobility

Among the most basic capabilities required of the working diver are his abilities to transport himself and a payload from one place to another, and to apply forces to tools or apparatus. Andersen (1969) provided some very basic measurements of swimming ability by having divers using SCUBA and wet suits swim a compass course at a depth of 20 feet while carrying various weights. Using wrist compasses, the subjects' best performance over the 780 foot course, off Scripps pier, was an error of less than 3 degrees, with an overall average error of about 4 degrees. Their speed over the course averaged between 1.2 and 1.3 knots while carrying 3, 6 or 9 pound weights (attached by a sling to their weight belts). The older, 1953, Cooperative Underwater Swimmer Project, found an average speed over a half mile course to be 0.96 knots. The slower speed of the CUSP divers is obviously due to the longer course, more cumbersome equipment, and possibly, to less efficient fins.

While the diver must on occasion drag heavy weights for short distances, he is typically asked to exert force while stationary at the work site. Although theoretically the unrestrained diver should experience great difficulty doing this because he is weightless, in practice he manages quite well by stabilizing himself on nearby structures or by applying force in quick movements. Special jobs such as drilling against metal may require a restraint harness, however.

The watery environment in itself seems to have little effect on strength. Only very slight losses in strength due to submersion could be found in a series of tests, involving lifting and pulling, administered to the SEALAB III aquanauts (Bowen, et al., 1966; Miller, 1966). Streimer (1969 a,b) also found statistically significant, but not large, reductions in power output of divers performing various cranking and push-pull exercises while they were submerged in a tank at moderate temperatures. Cold water has a somewhat greater effect. In a comprehensive study of diving performance in cold water, Bowen (1967) reported the following results on the average grip strength of 10 subjects:

Grip Strength (Kg)

Time after "gloves off"	Dry Land	62°F Water	47°F Water
2 min 10 sec	55.4	54.1	54.1
24 min 20 sec	55.4	52.1	47.4

We note that performance on the above tasks is generally not impaired as much as we might expect, although it does fall off markedly with time in the colder water. We shall see in the subsequent sections that the psycho-motor type of work task, and higher order mental tasks, suffer more under the stress of cold.

The ability of an individual to exert force underwater is closely related to his ability to exert force on the surface. In a study by Weltman and Egstrom (1969) an exercise test battery composed of surface bicycling, surface and underwater weight lifting, surface and underwater block moving, and underwater pipe structure assembly was administered to two 7-man groups of divers. High correlations were observed between levels of heart rate and inspiratory minute volume exhibited in various surface tests and the levels of these variables exhibited in strenuous underwater activity. A high degree of concordance was also observed among heart rate, inspiratory minute volume, and respiratory rate over the range of surface and underwater tests. (Figures 1 and 2 illustrate these findings.) Using the heart rate and respiratory volume measures, it was possible to order with respect to imposed workload tasks of known and unknown physical requirements. The main implications were that it is feasible to estimate under-

PHYSIOLOGICAL TEST		SURFACE					UNDERWATER			
		Rest	Leg 500	Leg 1000	Arm 400	Blocks	Rest	Arm 400	Blocks	Task
SURFACE	Rest		$.76^{+}$	$.78^{+}$	.65	.58	$^{-}.10$	$.94^{++}$	$.83^{+}$	.13
	Leg 500			$.85^{+}$	.65	$.72^{+}$	.12	$.87^{+}$	$.78^{+}$	.21
	Leg 1000				$.95^{++}$	.64	.47	$.92^{++}$	$.82^{+}$	.43
	Arm 400					$.78^{+}$	.60	$.79^{+}$	$.83^{+}$	.68
	Blocks						.12	.60	$.99^{++}$	.39
UNDERWATER	Rest							.19	.22	$.71^{+}$
	Arm 400								$.74^{+}$	.21
	Blocks									.25
	Task									

Figure 1: **Subject rank correlations between exercise tests, using heart rate as the physiological variable.**

Subject		r_s			Mean r_s
No.	I. D.	HR-MV	HR-RR	MV-RR	
1	29	$.92^{++}$	$.90^{++}$	$.77^{+}$	.86
2	25	$.92^{++}$	$.85^{++}$	$.92^{++}$	.87
3	27	$.68^{+}$	$.69^{+}$	$.79^{++}$	.72
4	24	$.81^{++}$	$.86^{++}$	.50	.72
5	6	$.97^{++}$	$.74^{+}$	$.68^{+}$	.80
6	28	$.90^{++}$	$.73^{+}$	$.87^{++}$	.83
7	30	$.82^{++}$	$.97^{++}$	$.71^{+}$	.83
Mean		.86	.82	.75	.81

$^{+}P < 0.05$

$^{++}P < 0.01$

Figure 2: **Rank correlations among different physiological variables for individual subjects over nine tests.**

water work capacity through surface tests, and that basic physiological measurements, particularly heart rate, taken during diving operations can permit reasonable estimations of imposed workload.

Other studies have indicated that as in surface work, there is a linear relationship underwater between heart rate and oxygen uptake. Figure 3 shows this relationship for several surface and submerged studies. The results suggest that heart rate monitoring in work situations provides an excellent indicator of diver energy expenditure. There may be some complicating factors however. Streimer (1969 b) has noticed a shift toward higher oxygen/pulse ratios with increasing depth. Moreover, investigators have reported a lower heart rate underwater for equivalent surface work.

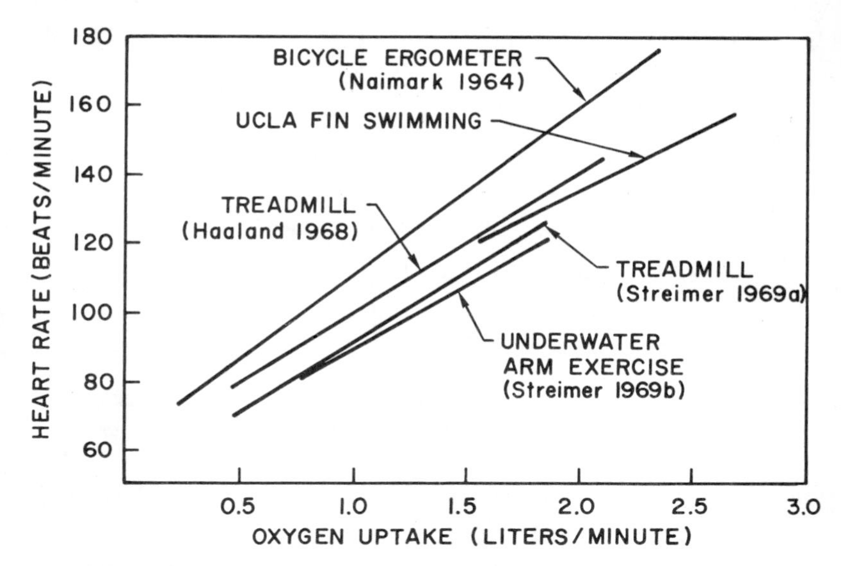

Figure 3: **Oxygen uptake versus heart rate for a number of dry land and underwater exercise studies.**

In Figure 4 is presented the average heart rate response in an exercise study conducted at UCLA (Weltman et al., 1968). The paced task consisted of raising and lowering a weight via pulleys, much like rowing. This involved arm movements and some involvement of the back muscles. Subjects wore faceplates and used single hose regulators (hose supplied) both in the 80°F to 85°F dry land runs and the 82°F water temperature tank runs. There was a significant decrease in heart rate underwater at rest, and a truly striking difference underwater with exercise; one subject exhibiting a decease of 62 beats/min. over dry land values after 5 minutes of exercise (172 to 110 beats/min.). Streimer, et al. (1969 b) showed similar results in self-paced tasks of rotary cranking and "hack sawing." The implication is that diver work tolerance values which depend on heart rate readings will have to be carefully calibrated in the actual work situations.

Visual Performance

We are normally almost entirely dependent on vision to make our way in the world. The diver, however, finds his visual capability severely curtailed by his equipment and his environment. Though he learns to anticipate poor vision and to compensate for it somewhat by touch and intuition, this curtailment does have a profound effect on his work methodology. Visual capability can be divided into two basic concepts: detection — the ability to observe the presence or absence of a target, and acuity — the finer discriminations, such as are required in reading.

One very basic problem in underwater detection is that of the restriction in peripheral vision resulting from the use of face plates or

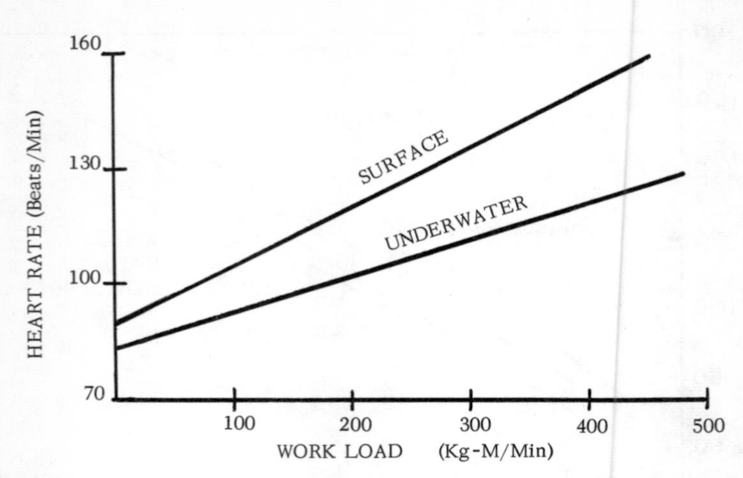

Figure 4: **Heart rate response to arm exercise on the surface and underwater (Waltman et al, 1968).**

diving helmets. The normal visual field in air varies among individuals, but is on the order of 60°-70° upward, 100° to either side, and 80° downward. With typical sport diving face plates underwater, the visual field contracts to about 60° upward, 50° to either side, and 10° downward (Weltman, et al., 1965). Simply replacing the face plate with a larger one has some inherent problems. A ray of light having an angle of incidence of 48.2° to an air-water interface (the glass makes a small difference) is totally reflected, thus limiting the field of view through a flat face plate (Barnard, 1961). The use of contact lenses provides a greater but still limited field of view but has several operational difficulties (Faust and Beckman, 1966).

Murkiness is the second major factor acting to degrade visual capacity. Duntley has developed a comprehensive system for predicting the visibility (detection) of underwater objects based upon water clarity (Duntley, et al., 1959). During SEALAB II (Miller, 1966) comparative tests were conducted which give a good general feel for underwater visibility at depth in relatively clear water. (Exact water clarity and lighting data are not available.) The SEALAB II aquanauts approached the targets until they could: 1) detect their presence and 2) identify their shape. A total of 20 observational trials were made; the results are summarized below:

TARGET	Black Circle	White Square	Yellow Triangle	White Cross
Target Area	707 cm^2	900 cm^2	900 cm^2	900 cm^2
Detection Distance	24.4 ft	18.3 ft	16.7 ft	16.5 ft
Recognition Distance	20.0 ft	14.2 ft	13.5 ft	13.4 ft

The working diver's ability to detect objects can be enhanced by painting them to take full advantage of local transmissivity. The transmittance of light underwater varies widely, depending upon the amount and nature of turbidity. Pure water has the greatest transmittance at 480 milli-microns, shifting toward the longer wavelenghs as the turbidity increases. Therefore the optimal color for the target detectability depends upon water conditions. Spherical buoys 20 cm in diameter had best visibility, viewed from underwater with natural illumination, when painted as follows (Kinney, et al., 1967):

a) For rivers, harbors, and other turbid bodies, fluorescent orange is best.

b) For coastal waters of mediocre clarity, fluorescent green and fluorescent orange are best.

c) For clear water, fluorescent green and white are best.

Kinney, et al., state that fluorescent paints are superior to non-fluorescent and white is overall the best non-fluorescent, although black has emerged as highly visible in some studies, such as the SEALAB II experiment. Lythgoe and Hemmings (1967) have shown that the use of polarizing filters in the face plate can improve the detectability of objects by increasing contrast ratios through reduction of polarized light scattered from particles in the water. In a field test off Malta, the use of such filters increased by 15 percent the distance of target detection. If so, this could significantly improve the diver's ability to do work, particularly under artificial illumination, which produces much task-scatter.

In addition to water turbidity, the diver must deal with the distortion produced by the air-glass-water interface of his mask. For small objects viewed nearly straight ahead, the retina receives an image subtending an angle which is larger than the physical angle by a factor of n/n'; where $n' = 1$ (the index of refraction of air) and $n = 1.3$ (the index of refraction of water). Thus the diver has his choice of perceiving the object either nearer or larger, or both. The resolution of this decision is one of the basic tenets of visual psycho-physics: the size-distance invariance hypothesis (Holway and Boring, 1941). Basically, with a given visual angle, if a subject knows the size of the object, he can make a good judgment of its distance.

When the object viewed is large, or is not normal to the air-water interface (the face plate), the refractive error becomes much larger. For example, a ray impinging upon the face plate at 45° from the normal will appear to come from 75° (Christianson, 1968). Therefore, if a diver looks directly at an object which subtends a physical angle of 90°, it will appear to subtend an arc of 150°, nearly filling his field of view, and it will appear to be 1.67 times its real size. Thus for large objects shape as well as size and distance will be distorted. Ross (1965) has determined that divers tend to overestimate size under ordinary circumstances, and to overestimate distance when the distance is large. Ross's conclusion was that size and distance judgments were "very erratic." But Ross (1968) and Ross et al. (1969) have also shown that divers can adapt to these visual distortions, that is, to make progressively more accurate estimates of true physical size and distance. Nevertheless, even the highly experienced diver retains some built-in error in his underwater visual judgments.

Cold and Work Performance

Although new types of equipment, such as the hot water suit, can provide the diver with adequate protection from ocean cold in certain situations, the typical diver still works with cold as a constant companion. Underwater cold is more debilitating than surface cold, because the higher conductivity of water essentially sucks heat from the body. There are two main effects, on psycho-motor performance and on mental function.

The diver's capability to perform psycho-motor tasks such as operate tools, run nuts, use shackles, tie knots — the most common variety of tasks — suffers rather important degradations in the ocean environment. Two measures are commonly used to assess diver performance in psycho-motor skills; how long it takes to complete a given task, and the errors committed in task performance. Bowen (1967) hypothesizes two types of effects on psychromotor performance: a "water" effect and a "cold" effect. A good example is the screw plate test. In this task, the subject is presented with a vertical plate having 16 holes. On one end of the plate eight holes have nuts and bolts through them. The task is to remove the nuts and bolts by hand and move them to the holes on the other half of the board. An error is scored if the subject drops a part or does not tighten a pair sufficiently. The average performance times for five subjects on dry land and three water temperatures are shown below:

Condition	Dry	72°F	62°F	47°F
Completion Time (Seconds)	69.44	78.12	84.09	90.36

The subjects wore SCUBA and 3/16" wet suits and were in the water for varying periods of time.

The "water" effect is illustrated by the 12½ percent increase in completion time found in warm, clear, shallow water. A similar result was exhibited in the diver performance program in SEALAB II, where sizable decrements in various psycho-motor tasks were observed over dry land values in clear, 72°F water at a depth of 15 feet (Bowen, 1966). The same type of effect was found on a tactile discrimination test, where the two point threshold more than doubled in 72°F water over dry land.

The "cold" effect is characterized by a decrease in performance with decreasing temperatures and with cumulative exposure. There is good evidence that this decrement is largely due to loss of hand sensitivity, and cooling of muscles and joints. For example, after 2½ minutes of "gloves off" in 47°F water, the tactile sensitivity threshold increased to approximately three times the dry land threshold. After about 25 minutes, it increased to nearly five times the dry land value, or an 0.96 inch separation (Bowen, 1967). Although the scores on a test such as this vary somewhat, depending upon the apparatus used, the impact is quite dramatic as regards the diver's degradation in such skills as identification of unseen knobs, handles or parts.

Regarding mental performance, Bowen (1968) reported that easy problem-solving tasks were almost unaffected by cold exposure. Cold had the most marked effect on immediate memory and attention. Consequently, it may significantly decrease diver ability to follow remembered instructions and to perform several tasks at once. In addition, mind-wandering and depersonalization phenomena may occur.

Bowen's subjects did not exhibit any sort of adaptation toward the environment, in fact they tolerated the cold less well as the tests went on. However, the SEALAB II aquanauts apparently learned to tolerate the cold more during their stay on the bottom (Miller, 1966). There is evidence (Stromme, et al., 1963) that people who work in the cold frequently develop both physiologic and psychologic tolerance to the stress. Motivation is a significant factor. As Radloff and Helmreich (1968) have pointed out from their psychological research during SEALAB II, good divers exhibit a truly amazing capability to adapt to a hostile environment when motivated to do so. For example, Vaughn (1968) reports the results of a study in which UDT and SEAL team personnel piloted a wet submersible for periods of 4 to 6 hours in 60°F water. Although deep body temperature fell by 2°F, control performance was not adversely affected. Nevertheless, Vaughn states that the combined factors of cold, poor vision, and some anxiety exaggerate the requirements for simplicity in the design of underwater displays, controls and maintenance procedures.

Attention and Anxiety

A common occurrence in underwater work is mistakes due to oversights, often of the simplest type — leaving things undone, forgetting equipment, not noticing critical signs, etc. These effects have appeared in experimental studies as well as on the job.

For example, several researchers (Kiessling and Maag, 1962, Baddeley, 1966, Adolfson, 1967) have shown performance decrements attributable to nitrogen narcosis for subjects in dry pressure chambers. When tested in the ocean at similar pressures, however, the performance decrements were much greater than in a dry pressure chamber (Baddeley, 1966). We might attribute this increased decrement to the "water" and "cold" effects found by Bowen (1967) except for one particular study by Baddeley (1967). When tests were performed at 5 feet and 100 feet in an exceptionally pleasant environment, where the divers entered the water from shore, swimming to the 100 foot level over a sloping rocky bottom, the decrement in performance between 5 and 100 feet was very slight. Why should the deep water effects not appear in this study when they were quite apparent in previous studies? Why should a professional diver make foolish errors in a simple job?

A good part of the answer may lie in anxiety, and in its effect on attention. Recent studies have indicated that a person's response to an environment he considers dangerous may involve a phenomenon called perceptual narrowing. Perceptual narrowing is a reduction in the ability to assimilate sensory information from the environment. It was observed by Berkun (1964) in simulated war games and other high risk environments. He reported that in the high risk environment, subjects performed poorly and failed to react to important stimuli.

A study in the Biotechnology Laboratory, UCLA, indicated that for novice divers, reaction time to a light in their visual periphery was progressively lengthened as they moved from the surface to a diving tank and to the open ocean, while central task performance was not changed (Weltman and Egstrom, 1966). It was hypothesized that anxiety associated with the more dangerous diving conditions caused the perceptual narrowing. In that study, however, we could only surmise that the affected subjects reacted to the tank and ocean as anxiety-producing situations. Further, it was uncertain whether the changes in peripheral response were also related to the physiological changes which accompany any submergence, and particularly, submergence in cold water.

In a second, more elaborate study, subjects were deceived into believing that a chamber in which they were sitting was being pressurized. These subjects, all non-divers, exhibited mild anxiety during their "descent" as evidenced by heart rate levels and by responses to a questionnaire. As in the diving study, a light was placed in the skirt of the diving mask. A central task, an automatic acuity tester, kept the subjects occupied while monitoring the secondary peripheral stimulus.

The "chamber" subjects performed the same as a control group on the central task, but their ability to detect the peripheral lights was reduced almost in half. The implication was that even mild anxiety can have a deep effect on attention and perception. It is reasonable to assume that in certain situations, experienced divers may undergo at least this much anxiety, if not more. If the perceptual effect is the same, it may influence significantly their ability to perform reliable, error-free work.

The Effects of Experience

Experience will obviously effect the way a diver reacts to his environment, and how he works within it. At UCLA, we have used a set of simulated diving tasks to examine the influence of experience on performance in tank and open ocean environments. This is done in part to help clarify the areas of complex performance which are most sensitive to variations in environment and diving capability, so that measurement techniques may subsequently be developed to focus on them.

The most recent version of the simulated diving task consists of several elements and focuses on the assembly, pressure test, and disassembly of a bolted pipe structure (shown in Figure 5). The pipe structure is fabricated of 2-inch galvanized pipe and is about 7-feet high on a 4-foot by 5-foot base. Three main sections of pipe and the valve manifold are connected using ½-inch nuts and bolts and a specified combination of gaskets. The pipe sections weigh up to 50 pounds, and generally require both team members working in unison to position

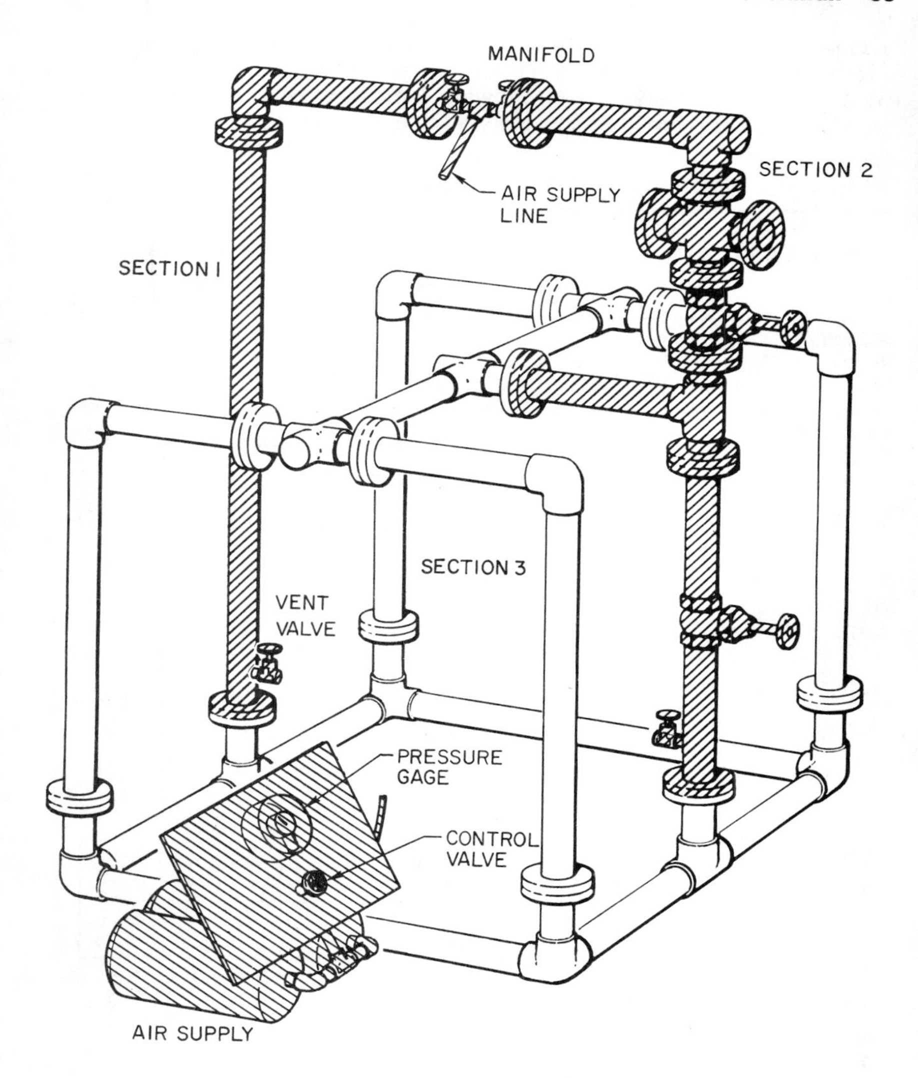

Figure 5: **The UCLA pipe construction task and associated pressure test console.**

them and bolt them together. The structure is then dewatered by use of the pressure console shown in Figure 5, checked for leaks, and disassembled. Before assembly and after disassembly subjects perform "paper and pencil" problem sets (such as problems in diving physics). This system, which we call the pipe puzzle, has been used for several experiments. We can only summarize some of the major results in this paper.

One study of interest involved a comparison of novice divers and experienced divers in the tank and in the ocean at 15-foot depths (Weltman, et al., 1969). The following table shows the average completion times for the pipe puzzle and the problem sets.

MEAN TASK COMPLETION TIME (MINUTES)

TASK	Experienced Diver Teams		Novice Diver Teams	
	Tank	Ocean	Tank	Ocean
Assemble Pressure Test and Disassemble	22.4	23.1	35.9	45.2
Problem Sets	11.1	8.6	13.2	9.2

Novices were about 60 percent slower than the experienced teams on the pipe puzzle in the tank. In the ocean, their times increased by another 26 percent, resulting in task completion times about twice those of the experienced group, which had not changed significantly between tank and ocean. For the pipe puzzle, then, lack of diving experience was reflected both in poorer overall performance, and a marked degradation even with mild ocean exposure.

Sampled activity analysis revealed why the experienced divers were performing better. Figure 6, for example, indicates how the experi-

ACTIVITY	Experienced Diver Teams		Novice Diver Teams	
	Tank N=5	Ocean N=5	Tank N=12	Ocean N=6
Fit bolt, nut, gasket	31.7	37.5	30.4	35.9
Hold part or tool	26.5	23.6	26.8	21.3
Torque bolt	20.6	21.3	17.1	21.8
Move part or tool	13.2	12.5	13.2	9.9
Communicate	1.0	0.6	3.6	4.1
Read instructions	0.5	0.0	1.0	0.0
Idle/Observe	1.0	1.2	4.0	4.1
Travel empty	5.5	3.3	3.9	2.9
TOTAL %	100.0	100.0	100.0	100.0
(Total Number of Tallies)	(1795)	(1850)	(882)	(587)

Figure 6: **Percent of time spent in various assembly activities by experienced and novice diver teams during shallow water experiments.**

enced and novice teams spent their time during pipe structure assembly. The most significant finding was that the advantage of the experienced divers was not in working faster, but in spending less time doing non-productive activities such as checking instructions, communications, idle observation. In fact, both groups hurried where they could in the ocean, probably in an effort to cut short the less pleasant runs. This showed up in the smaller problem set completion time, and may have contributed to the poorer problem-solving performance exhibited in the ocean by both groups (Figure 7).

SUMMARY OF PROBLEM SOLVING PERFORMANCE (PERCENT CORRECT)				
TEST	Experienced Diver Teams		Novice Diver Teams	
	Tank (N=5)	Ocean (N=5)	Tank (N=10)	Ocean (N=7)
Dive Questions				
Pre-Test	90	83	87	52
Post-Test	93	77	60	57

Figure 7: **Summary of problem solving performance (percent correct) by experienced and novice diver teams during shallow water experiments.**

In a follow up study, we selected a group of eight very experienced divers (by University standards) and compared their performance in the tank and in the ocean under somewhat more severe conditions. Every attempt was made to make the tank environment similar to the ocean. The tank was cooled to 60°F, made dark, and the water clouded. The ocean dives were conducted off a pier in 50 feet of water. The results matched very closely those of the previous study. Ocean completion times averaged a bit slower, while problem solution time showed a marked decrease in the ocean. Problem errors were slightly more frequent in the ocean environment.

The conclusions were that for experienced divers there is virtually no "ocean effect," at least at moderate depths, for the over-all aspects of complex tasks, but there may be some negative effect on problem solving. The implications are that novice divers should be eliminated from serious diving studies, and that tank simulations using experienced divers can substitute for costlier ocean runs in many instances. The definition of "novice" and "experienced," of course, may change as deeper, more hazardous exposures are considered.

WORK PERFORMANCE ON A LARGE-SCALE TASK

Divercon I

We have discussed influences on diver work performance in terms of particular skills and in simulations of whole task projects (the pipe puzzle). The next level of study is the observation of actual on-going diver work programs. The following represents one of the first attempts to perform a human factors analysis of a large scale operation. Of necessity we were as concerned about the methodology as with the results. (A full account of the program is available in a separate report: Weltman, et al., 1969).

At the time the study was undertaken, the U.S. Navy SEALAB III Project planned to establish an underwater habitat 600 feet deep off San Clemente Island, California. The habitat would be occupied successively by five teams of eight or nine men apiece, each team undertaking some special task in addition to its normal duties. For example, Team 2 was to demonstrate underwater salvage techniques, Team 3 was to construct a dry underwater shelter. The performance measurements made on Team 3 during the course of the shallow water trials, undertaken to prove the feasibility and to establish baseline performance levels for the Devercon I construction task is the concern of this section of the report.

Divercon I was developed and fabricated by the Naval Civil Engineering Laboratory at Port Hueneme, California. In it a tethered lift device was used to pick up and position over an anchor block the component parts of an underwater shelter. The shelter itself was a domed cylinder, open at the bottom, about 10 feet in diameter and 10 feet high. It was assembled underwater from parts consisting of: the bottom ring, to which were attached three supporting legs; the center ring; and the domed top. A buoyant lamp chandelier was "hung" above the entire assembly. The lift device was also buoyant, and contained a hydraulic winch operated from a separate control console. Divercon I was quite a test of diving abilities, involving control, communication, fine manipulation and heavy work, and because of its developmental nature, a substantial amount of problem solving.

Performance Measurement

Performance measurement occurred during two shallow water trials which took place in July 1968 and August 1968, at a depth of 50 feet off Anacapa Island, California. The six Navy and civilian members of Team 3 operated in July from a small air umbilical, using a light helmet, wet suit and fins. In August they used Navy Mark VIII gear and a larger umbilical containing a hot water line, essentially the equipment planned for the SEALAB exposure. Procedural recording was accomplished through the use of diver observers, work load was estimated by heart rate measurement, and supplemental information on relative task difficulties was gathered by questionnaire.

For the July trials, procedural recording was attempted using a single diver observer, who was familiar with the operations schedule, to record the activities of the working team on a plastic notepad and pencil. This approach, which had sufficed previously, proved inadequate for the complex, changing, Divercon I task. Aside from such factors as cold, isolation, information overload, which tended to limit the observer's output, the main difficulty was that while the observer was able to determine what the work team was doing, he could not likewise deermine *why* they were doing it. Consequently his report focused on actions rather than operations, and was poorly translatable into detailed procedural record. The problem was solved in the August trials by transferring responsibility for assembling the real-time procedural record from the observer-diver to a surface observer, who integrated, at a central station, work information from several sources. These included written notes, supplied by another surface person, on the latest changes in the operations plan and on the conversations between the working divers and their control station. His information inputs also included a TV picture from a camera hand-held by the diver-observer, and spoken comments by the diver-observer in response to surface questions. The diver-observer remained a key element in the system, and there were significant differences in his contribution depending on his diving experience and ease in the water.

Work Methodology

In both July and August, the divers spent about 12 hours on the bottom, but more was accomplished in the latter trials. Comparison of completion times for equivalent task elements revealed that the August values were 25 percent lower. Thus it appeared that any additional encumberance of the Mark VIII gear and umbilicals was more than offset by the effects of learning and improved cold protection from the hot water suits. Some representative values are presented below.

WORK COMPLETION TIMES (Minutes)

	JULY	AUGUST
Set up site. Rig lift device.	34.5	26.0
Position lower ring.	58.0	47.5
Position middle ring.	57.0	31.5
Position top ring.	64.0	54.0
Total	213.5	159.0

The following table summarizes how the divers spent their time during the August run. It indicates that even after practice, a considerable amount of time (about 33 percent) was spent nonproductively in correction, unfouling, or inactivity. Corrective efforts were activities which corrected mechanical or procedural faults; for example, finding and fixing leaks, and repositioning plugs and connectors. Idle time involved awaiting topside activities or communicating passively wth topside. Unfouling was time spent in untangling lines and diver umbilicals.

CLASSIFICATION OF UNDERWATER WORK ACTIVITIES FOR AUGUST DIVERCON RUN

	MINUTES	PERCENT TIME
Scheduled Work Elements		
General tasks	296	47
Life device control	111	17
Corrective Efforts	117	19
Unfouling Lines	52	8
Idle or Communicating	59	9
Total	634	100

How hard did the divers work during the construction job? The following table summarizes the heart rate data available from the August trials. The recording period has been divided into pre-dive, dive, and post-dive intervals. Constituent activities are identified during each. Constituent activities are identified during each. Classification of the dive task elements was somewhat arbitrary. For example, light work involved operating the control console, inspecting, shackling, and idle time; medium work involved swimming, cleaning plugs and connectors, untangling lines, and connecting electrical or pneumatic cables. Heavy work included lifting, pushing, pulling, torquing nuts or bolts with wrench, swimming with heavy objects, and shackling heavy lines such as the chandelier hold down chains. The entries for minimum, maximum, and average also reflect some arbitrary decisions in data analysis. On the whole, they are representative of work periods during which the heart rate had stabilized. The average represents modal value, rather than the arithmetic mean.

DIVERCON HEART RATES
(Beats/Minute)

	MIN.	MAX.	AVG.
Pre-Dive			
Rest (standing)	90	116	100
Put on Gear	78	124	107
Walk to Fantail	124	150	140
Dive			
Light Tasks	80	138	103
Medium Tasks	86	160	121
Heavy Tasks	99	160	137
Post-Dive			
Exit Water	138	180	160
Walk to Seat	153	168	160
Take off Gear	122	138	129

The heart rates for the light dive tasks were about the same as those obtained for the pipe construction task previously characterized as imposing a mild physiological stress. Experienced divers exhibited mean heart rates of about 96 beats/minute while assembling and disassembling that structure in the ocean. Using the light-task data as a bench mark, then, the present results indicated that the Divercon divers were undergoing substantial physiological loadings during medium and heavy task execution. An average heart rate of 137 beats/minute, for example, with a group maximum of 160 beats/minute, equals rates observed in a previous tank study for a strenuous block moving task and an arm exercise task involving a work output of 450 kgm./min. Sustained heart rate of 140 beats/minute was also observed in a brief examination of the Divercon task during January 1968. Data obtained during periods of underwater rest and light activity during the Divercon trials indicate heart rates are not appreciably raised by psychological factors. Streimer (1969) has suggested that divers will self-limit their work output underwater to light levels (heart rate around 100 to 110). Our data shows that this is not necessarily the case. Job demands may place quite heavy loads on individual divers.

Moreover, the data suggest that the most critical period from the cardiovascular standpoint may immediately follow the dive. Leaving the water and walking back to his seat carrying perhaps 150 lbs of Mark VIII rig and helmet, the average diver exhibited heart rates of 160 beats/minute, quite high for men in good physical condition. These evaluated rates may well reflect incomplete readaptation from the reduced hydrostatic stress accompanying underwater exposure. In any case such exertion imposed on cold and tired men provides some basis for concern, and suggests the need for rapid unloading of the emerging diver either by manual or mechanical means.

CONCLUSIONS

This paper has explored a number of factors which influence the diver in his ability to perform work; it has left out a good number more. A significant question, both for now and for the future, is: which factors are most important? One way of answering this is to examine the opinions of men engaged in open-ocean diving programs. We did just that, in conjunction with the diver observation program of the SEALAB III trials. Post dive questionnaires were administered to the members of the construction and salvage teams. Perhaps the most useful questionnaire, of the three we tried, required the divers to rank 10 diving factors in order of importance to successful task completion. A rank of one indicates the most important and a rank of ten the least important of the factors offered. The results are tabulated below:

MEAN RANK OF IMPORTANCE OF DIVING FACTORS

Diving Factor	Diver Construction Tasks (August Trials)	Salvage Operations
InterDiver Communication	2.3	6.5
Special Tools or Equipment	4.0	7.1
Cold Protection	4.2	4.9
Freedom of Movement	4.3	3.6
Current, Sea State, Depth	4.3	5.7
Visibility	5.0	4.8
Diver Strength/Endurance	7.0	4.5
Diver Buoyancy	7.2	5.9
Diver Stabilization	8.0	5.2
Communication to Surface	8.7	6.8

The team members agreed among themselves regarding the rankings, but the two team rankings differed in several respects. The salvage group seemed rather "diver centered." Factors dealing with the individual's ability to perform were judged most important; those involving inter-diver or diver-surface communication, or diving aids, were judged least important. What might be termed the environmental factors occupied an intermediate position. The Divercon group had a somewhat different outlook, and they also tended to agree better among themselves. This group stressed inter-diver communication and special tools, and assigned relatively low positions to strength and endurance. The effect of cold was also judged important. Both groups depreciated communications to the surface, reflecting either the dictum to "solve problems on the bottom," or the poor state of existing communications facilities. There was no significant correlation between judgments of the salvage group and those of the Divercon group.

On the whole, the responses seemed a reasonable reflection of the "team" nature of Divercon I, against the more individualistic demands of the salvage tasks. Except that in some major points, the opinion of both groups was at distinct odds with that of the observer. In Divercon I, for example, diver strength and endurance was ranked low, although many elements of the job seemed to require these abilities. Communications to the surface was judged least important, yet much of the shallow water trials depended on this facility. The salvage divers also showed this tendency. Diver stabilization was ranked low in the electric tools task, yet successful performance patently depended on this factor.

Why this decrepancy? One reason may be that researchers are as yet still communicating imperfectly with divers. Another may be that divers envision an "ideal" work situation, as well as an actual one, and their answers represent some combination of the two. Still another is that the factors are really task-dependent. But the one we would like to emphasize at the end of this paper is that although we know a fair amount about the constituent aspects of underwater work — those which can be broken out in controlled experiments — we know far too little about underwater work as it is actually performed. To acquire this knowledge, necessary to any improvements in work methodology, researchers must interact closely with "real world" diving operations more than they have done in the past. At UCLA, we hope to make such interaction the main thrust of our program for the next few years.

REFERENCES

Adolfson, J., "Human Performance and Behavior in Hyperbaric Environments." *Acta Psychologica Gothoburgensia,* VI, Almqvist and Wiksell, Stockholm, 1967.

Anderson, G. G., "Measurement of Scuba Diver Performance in an Open Ocean Environment." *American Society of Mechanical Engineers,* 69-UNT-2, New York, 1969.

Baddeley, A. D., "Influence of Depth on the Manual Dexterity of Free Divers: A Comparison Between Open Sea and Pressure Chamber Testing." *J. Appl. Psychol.,* 50 (1):81-85, 1966.

Baddeley, A. D., "Diver Performance and the Interaction of Stresses." in: Lythgoe, J. N., and Woods, J. D. (eds.), *Underwater Association Report 1966-67,* T. V. W. Industrial and Research Promotions Ltd., 45 Mount Park, Carshalton, Surry, England, 1967.

Barnard, E. E. P., "Visual Problems Underwater." *Proc. Royal Soc. Med.,* 54:9-10, 1961.

Berkun, M. M., "Performance Decrement Under Psychological Stress." Human Factors, 6 (1):21-30, 1964.

Bowen, H. M., Andersen, B., and Promisel, D., "Studies of Divers' Performance During the SEALAB II Project." *Human Factors,* 8 (3):183-199, 1966.

Bowen, H. M., "Diver Performance and the Effects of Cold." BSD No. 67-441, Dunlap and Associates, Inc., Darien, Connecticut, 1967.

Christianson, R. A., Weltman, G., and Egstrom, G. H., "Thrust Forces in Underwater Swimming." *Human Factors,* 7 (6):561-568, 1965.

Christianson, R. A., "A Study of Visual Acuity Underwater Using an Automatic Landolt Ring Presentation Technique." Report No. X8-128/020, Ocean Systems Operations, North American Rockwell Corp., Long Beach, California, 1968.

"Cooperative Underwater Swimmer Project." NAS-NRC, Committee on Amphibious Operations, San Diego, California (AD 416138), 1953.

Duntley, S. Q., Tyler, J. E., and Taylor, J. H., "Field Test of a System for Predicting Visibility by Swimmers from Measurements of Clarity of Natural Waters." Scripps Institution of Oceanography, Ref, 59-39, June 1959.

Faust, K. J., and Beckman, E. L., "Evaluation of a Swimmers Contact Air-Water Lens System." *Military Medicine,* 131 (9):779-788, 1966.

Haaland, J. E., "Use of Simple Physiological Measurements in Obtaining Relative Energy Expenditure and Workloads During a Simulated Lunar Surface Mission." *Aerospace Medicine,* 39 (2):153-157, 1968.

Holway, A. H., and Boring, E. G., "Determinants of Apparent Visual Size with Distance Variant." *Am. J. Psychol.,* 54:21-37, 1941.

Kent, P. R., and Weissman, S., "Visual Resolution Underwater." Report No. 476, Submarine Medical Research Laboratory, U. S. Naval Submarine Medical Center, Submarine Base, Groton, Connecticut, 1966.

Kiessling, R. J., and Maag, C. H., "Performance Impairment as a Function of Nitrogen Narcosis." *J. Appl. Psychol.,* 46 (2):91-95, 1962.

Kinney, J. A. S., et al., "Visibility of Colors Underwater." *J. Opt. Soc. Am.,* 57 (6):802-809, 1967.

Lythgoe, J. N., and Hemmings, C. C., "Polarized Light and Underwater Vision." *Nature,* 213:893-894, 1967.

Miller, J. W., "The Measurement of Human Performance: SEALAB II." in: *Transactions of the Joint Symposium: Man's Extension Into the Sea,* Marine Technology Society, Washington, D.C., January 1966.

Naimark, A. Wasserman, K., and McIlroy, M. B., "Continuous Measurement of Ventlatory Exchange Ratio During Exercise." *J. Appl. Physiol.,* 19 (4):644-652, 1964.

Radloff, R., and Helmreich, R., *Groups Under Stress: Psychological Research in SEALAB II.* Appleton-Century-Crofts, New York, 1968.

Ross, H. E., "Size and Distance Judgements Underwater and on Land." in: Lythgoe, J. N., and Woods, J. D. (eds.), *Symposium of the Underwater Association for Malta 1965,* T. G. W. Industrial and Research Promotions, Ltd., 45 Mount Park, Marshalton, Surry, England, 1965.

Streimer, I., "A Study of Work-Producing Characteristics of Underwater Operations." Report No. SD 69-20, Life Sciences Branch, Space Division, North American Rockwell Corp., Downey, California, February 1969 (a).

Streimer, I., "A Study of Work-Producing Characteristics of Underwater Operations as a Function of Depth." Report No: SD 69-712, Life Sciences Branch, Space Division, North American Rockwell Corp., Downey, California, November 1969 (b).

Stromme, S., Lange Anderson, K., and Elsner, R. W., "Metabolic and Thermal Responses to Muscular Exertion in the Cold." *J. Appl. Physiol.,* 18 (3):756-763, 1963.

Vaughan, W. S. Jr., "Diver Performance and Endurance in a Wet Submersible." Whittenburg, Voughn Associates, Unpublished paper, 1968.

Weltman, G., Christianson. R. A., and Egstrom, G. H., "Visual Fields of the SCUBA Diver." *Human Factors,* 7 (5):423-430, 1965.

Weltman, G., and Egstrom, G. H., "Perceptual Narrowing in Novice Divers." *Human Factors,* 8 (6):499-506, 1966.

Weltman, G., Egstrom, G. H., Elliott, R. E., and Stevenson, H. S., "Underwater Work Measurement Techniques: Initial Studies." Report No. 68-11, Biotechnology Laboratory, University of California, Los Angeles, 1968.

Weltman, G., Egstrom, G. H., Christianson, R. A., and Crooks, T. P., "Underwater Work Measurement Techniques: 1968 Studies." Report No. 69-19, Biotechnology Laboratory, University of California, Los Angeles, 1969.

REACTION 1
Third Session

W. S. Vaughan, Jr., Ph.D.
President, Oceanautics, Inc.
Alexandria, Virginia

INTRODUCTION

First, I want to congratulate Dr. Weltman for an excellent paper summarizing current research findings about the factors that affect man's work in underwater environments. The paper includes a wide range of material and is a well-documented survey.

Second, I want to present some data, collected in an at-sea environment, that point-up the importance of two of the many factors that affect man's performance in the undersea: training/habituation, and equipment characteristics.

TRAINING/HABITUATION

I'm convinced that in order to obtain a *true* estimate of man's *potential* performance in tasks underwater, measurement should continue over a reasonably long period of time. The worker needs time to get the hang of the job. He needs time to get used to the *specific* equipment and procedures, and he needs to get habituated or accustomed to the conditions.

Between June and December, 1967, we had 7 UDT/SEAL team personnel as an experimental group to evaluate a new Navy wet submersible. For 24 weeks these men trained in the operation of the vehicle. We were interested in their learning curves, rates of skill acquisition, and upper limits of performance in areas that included:

- Depth and course control
- Acoustic homing
- DR navigation

A final four weeks were set aside to test cold exposure effects. We made six 4-hour runs and three 6-hour runs in the ocean at 58-60° F. We took continuous measures of skin and core temperature as well as vehicle performance outputs. Core temperatures fell as expected in 58-60° F water as a function of the thickness of the man's subcutaneous fat. In the thinner subjects the fall was as much as 1.67° C, but *in no case did performance degrade.* The tasks were reasonably complex, involving short-term memory and psychomotor tracking components. The subjects were so well trained in the task and so accustomed to the environmental conditions, that task performance levels were maintained over six hours of exposure.

Equipment Characteristics

Performance measures descriptive of what man can do are highly dependent on how well the equipment he must use accommodates his sensory, perceptual, and control characteristics. Acoustic homing accuracy and, therefore, vehicle control of heading became a critical performance area in the operational context in which we were working. The homing system used in training consisted of a wide angled hydrophone mounted on the bow of the vehicle, a variable frequency receiver, and a bone phone. Available pingers were used as the sound source and the system gave generally erratic performance. We decided to look into this problem more systematically, and identified received horizontal beam width and pinger information rate as the critical variables affecting performance. We varied receiver horizontal beam angle at 15° and 5°. We had pingers made at 1 pps, 3 pps, 8 pps, and CW.

A test range was constructed which consisted of a 40 foot line marked off in 5 feet intervals by buoys. The line was anchored at the ends. Two such measurement systems were installed at an interval of 1,000 yards.

A group of submersible operators was given five hours of training in acoustic homing and then the experimental test program was begun. Results showed that precision of homing was increased by using narrower beam widths in the receiver and by using high information rate sound sources as a target. Average miss distance was 12 feet for the 15°, and 7 ft. for the 5° beam widths. As pinger repetition rates were increased from 1, 3, and 8 pulses per second to continuous wave, average miss distance decreased from 18, 14, and 10 to 5 feet.

This single receiver system was augmented by adding a swivelled hydrophone operated by the no. 2 man in the submersible. This feature reduced average miss distance from 5 feet. to 3 feet, but more importantly, tightened the range of scores from a 35 feet miss to a 15 feet miss.

Finally we shifted from an auditory read-out of the signal to a visual read-out. Instead of guiding on judgments of relative amplitude, the pilot could guide on a meter needle. Average miss distance with this system was ½ foot and full error range was 2½ feet.

The point is perhaps over illustrated. The answer to the question, "How accurately can a man home on an acoustic signal?" depends on the characteristics of the equipment he is provided to support the performance.

REACTION 2
Third Session

Hugh A. Bowen, Ph.D.
Managing Scientist
Dunlap & Association, Inc.
Darien, Conn.

Dr. Weltman has written a valuable and timely review of the state of research concerning the impact of entering the watery environment on the human diver. There can be no doubt that the behavioral repertoire of man is changed, modified, impaired, and constrained in multiple ways and in varying degrees dependent upon the particular diving conditions and the tasks to be performed.

I am pleased that Dr. Weltman concentrated on "extrabaric" factors and was concerned to demonstrate that there are a range of effects (and hence problems and hence needed solutions) in the shallow regime of diving. We may be seeing — I will surmise — a decrease in emphasis for going "deeper for longer" and a new emphasis on diver effectiveness in shallower conditions where most of the diver's work is to be found.

The issue of diver effectiveness will be, I suggest, the paramount issue in the immediate future. A major deterrent to spending the large sums needed to provide life support equipment and services to a diver is his ineffectiveness as a worker at depth. There are a number of limitations operating to reduce work effectiveness as a function of depth.

Interestingly these are not attributable primarily to changes in the diver himself but rather the conditional impairment on his behavior repertoire. He is enclosed, encumbered, and tethered by his life support equipment. His sensory modalities are handicapped or made inoperative. He is likely to be cold. He is dependent upon a system of decompression to return him safely to the surface. He is relatively isolated and highly dependent upon his own resources to get him out of difficulties; and difficulties can develop and become critical very quickly. All these encumbrances and contingencies multiply as a function of depth. They serve to limit the deep diver as much as or more than the limitations imposed by the ability of the tissues to accept hyperbarism or the capabiliy to prevent or guard against the secondary effects and hazards of the hyperbaric state.

A major consequence of the state in which a diver finds himself — even a shallow diver — is pinpointed by Dr. Weltman. "The deep sea diver generally performs quite commonplace work." Dr. Weltman goes on to state that the jobs required are relatively simple and no more than a mechanic would be expected to do routinely and easily on dry land. In fact, the situation often is much more drastic. Dive masters make great efforts to reduce the divers' tasks to the simplest possible, compatible with getting the job done. The costs of diving are so high that it appears to be cost beneficial to have the assurance of the diver achieving a simple step when down below, rather than attempt anything which is at all complex in a behavior sense. Behavioral complexity is risky because it increases the chances of error or fault and non-completion.

SOURCES OF IMPAIRMENT

The great virtue of the research that Dr. Weltman has accumulated in his paper is to make explicit some of the sources of impairment and the nature of the impairments on the human. Some of the changes that occur are more or less unique to the water environment; for instance, the changes brought about in perception by the magnification effect, water turbidity, changes in color, also such effects as neutral buoyancy, viscosity, and the thermal effects. These effects and many others constitute the environmental and situational stress on the diver. We can witness the same type of changes in the diver as have been reported elsewhere to characterize the human response to stress. In terms of initial disorganization of behavior, we can expect certain higher cognitive processes to be affected. Specifically, we can expect disturbances in short-term appropriate concentration of attention and in flexibility of attention. These are typically vulnerable processes when the individual is exposed to environmental and situational stress. We are, I believe, at the beginning of a period when we are able to show that these processes are, indeed, those that are affected; and that the disturbances serve to diminish the capability of the diver. These effects are generic and central and are both a consequence of and additive to the more direct kinds of impairments caused by equipment encumbrance, the tractionless state, which Dr. Egstrom has referred to in his paper.

Memory Support Capability

In viewing these papers, I am most inclined to conclude that it would be useful to supplement our concepts and efforts with respect to diver "Life Support Systems" with a parallel effort to develop diver "Behavioral Support Systems." I envisage a continuum at one end of which would be "Death Prevention Measures" and at the other end would be some measure or device which would provide (let us say) "Memory Support Capability." I have not invented such a device yet. Maybe something very simple is required. On other occasions something more sophisticated and complex may be appropriate. Perhaps the proper concept is to have available an inventory of "Behavioral Support" devices which can be packaged into a specific Behavioral Support Subsystem appropriate to whatever the work mission happens to be. These ideas grow out of reading through Dr. Weltman's paper because, it seems to me, there is a strong implication in the work reviewed.

It is, briefly, that we have not yet learned to preserve more than a small amount of the full human potential in the water environment. We have learned to pressurize and depressurize the human so that we can place him in the water. We have shown he can do simple tasks and we use this capability. But, we are far from having the full human behavior repertoire at our disposal underwater. I hope that as we learn more about what happens to the human diver there will be a consistent effort to allow the diver to behave as widely and variously as possible and to re-equip him (as it were) with effective sense modalities, communication means, response and effector capabilities; and finally, to decriticalize the hazard of diving so that the pre-occupation and/or anxiety over one's integrity is removed to normal levels.

REACTION 3
Third Session

John T. Quirk
Naval Civil Engineering Laboratory
Port Hueneme, Calif.

This paper was reviewed by five engineers working in the general field of diver tools and work systems at the Naval Civil Engineering Laboratory, Port Hueneme, California, and they consider it to be an excellent compilation and observation of the present scene.

The following comments are offered primarily as supplemental information and to reinforce suggestions for future work.

STRENGTH AND MOBILITY

Additional information has just been published (TR-653, "Diver Performance Using Handtools and Hand-Held Pneumatic Tools")* describing recent work at the Naval Civil Engineering Laboratory. The results indicate the level of axial force that a diver can exert in a drilling type situation. Tests were conducted using one and two arms with the divers working on vertical, overhead, and deck like surfaces where no natural handholds or footholds existed. Tethering equipment was used for diver restraint during the two-arm tests. Diver force ranged from 17.5 to 35.4 pounds for one-arm tests and 32.3 to 80.4 pounds for two arms with tethering.

COLD AND WORK PERFORMANCE

We would like to emphasize the conclusion of Dr. Vaughan, that the combined factors of cold, poor vision, and some anxiety exaggerate the requirements for simplicity in the design of underwater displays, controls, and procedures. We attempt to be "painfully simple" in our designs.

ATTENTION AND ANXIETY

We concur with the results discussed and also suggest that an additional factor contributing to the occurrence of simple mistakes is common fatigue.

THE EFFECTS OF EXPERIENCE

Again, we concur with the statement that for experienced divers there is virtually no "ocean effect" at moderate depths. This was also one of our conclusions based on tank versus ocean comparisons reported in TR-653, "Diver Performance Using Handtools and Hand-Held Pneumatic Tools."

WORK PERFORMANCE ON A LARGE SCALE TASK

Dr. Weltman correctly observes the task dependency influence in the ranking of importance of diving factors by the construction team and salvage team. However, what is not evident from the data is the marked difference in experience, both type and amount, of the two groups of divers. This difference of general experience was significant and would further confound attempts to draw specific conclusions from this information.

It is now time to move toward the "real world" as Dr. Weltman indicates and the following suggestions are made to aid this effort.

1. Gain the divers' confidence. They must understand and, if possible, see results that indicate the researcher is on "their side" and can and will help them do their work in a safer, more effective manner.
2. Really listen. The divers will very frequently provide the solutions to equipment and work method problems.
3. If you do not use their suggestions, explain why — feed back.
4. Know your divers, their specific experience, types of diving and training.
5. Minimize use of questionnaires. We have found a tape-recorded interview to be a very effective way to obtain information once confidence is established.

Acknowledgements

The review of this paper was significantly assisted by my colleagues Mr. F. B. Barrett, Mr. S. B. Black, Lieutenant (jg) R. Elliott, and Mr. L. Liffick.

---

* Appendix describing this test will be found on page 155.

DISCUSSION
Third Session

Dr Bradner: At the present time, why don't we break into questions. I would like to try to get you people to resummarize briefly what the question is, because yesterday we did not get this on the record and we probably should. I'll try to remember to insist that you do so. If any of you have remarks that you wish to make or, put in the record, let me invite you to come up and grab the mike. This way you can be recorded. Questions, then. Yes?

Audience question: What is a "can do" job?

Mr. Quirk: The syndrome of the can-do or easy job allows the man to get the work done. I'm sure this is true. It's a positive attitude, but by refusing to admit that it's hard, or how it could be made easier, he's retarding the growth in the industry. He's keeping his job, as Bev Morgan spoke yesterday, because if he starts to say it's hard, they'll get another guy because of the competition in the commercial end.

Audience question: Is there a place for marine technology training programs in junior-colleges?

Dr. Bradner: I think that remark is worth repeating as the summary problem.

Mr. Quirk: The gentleman describes himself as in the marine technology course at Santa Barbara City College which I'm familiar with and it is a very excellent course. It is aimed at producing an all-around marine technician, not just a diver, but an all-around marine technician. My comments toward the specialized worker relate to the people who are really, who are just diving and doing the proper jobs, I would say, the more specialized jobs. Now, as I referred to the Panama Canal company, everybody did do the general, easy work. But when the tougher jobs came up, they did get the specialists in that area. So I would say that you're on the right track and you will have a better and more mobile type of job, or easier to get a job. With a wider background you will probably have a specialty later.

Audience question: What is the outlook for the two-year trained marine technician?

Mr. Quirk: To repeat the question, what is the outlook for the two-year trained marine technician in the immediate future at the Santa Barbara City College and the other schools?

Now, I'm not familiar with the other courses, but I assume they're similar. Personally, speaking for myself, I would like to have some of those fellows with us. We've run into administrative problems, a lack of understanding at the upper levels with the requirements of people like that. We know we need them but we have a selling job, which I've been working on for a number of months with our middle manager. It is very difficult. I don't know commercially what the outlook is. I think the other gentlemen can give you a better outlook at what the commercial opportunities are.

Audience question: What can you suggest to provide a diver in order to support his behavior?

Dr. Bowen: The question was that the concept of the behavioral support system is a new one and if I had my way what could I suggest to provide a diver with in order to support his behavior.

Basically my point of view is that the diver should meet two requirements. He should be unencumbered as possible and he should be able to get the job done. Those two requirements are very often in conflict, so that there's a trade-off. We are very used to this in the aerospace business. For instance, you look at the mission or job to be done — the conditions or the situation — you devise a system, you mobilize a system, or you design one to meet these requirements.

Let me take one aspect of a diving operation, namely, transportation. A number of things need transportation both vertically and laterally. Probably, the worst resource in many respects is the human for transporting any kind of goods or objects. He is a very inefficient transportation device, so that one wishes to provide him with things which will help to effect transportation of objects. There are a number of possible things that you can do. Some of them are very simple — possibly not terribly effective — such as flotation bags which at least takes away the weight aspect. There are other solutions that Dr. Baum was obviously describing. One of them is, STV, transportation of personnel by vehicle. One has to look at what is required, what are the problems, what the resources are available and devise a system which will meet these requirements. Probably each one of us could expand on that general philosophy and begin to devise systems which would meet the requirements, both general on the one hand and the kind of requirements talked about to some extent yesterday, namely, vision rate requirements. One of the obvious things to try to improve is the face mask, and people have been improving that. These are general requirements, and then there are the specific requirements. I believe you should be able to pick out suitable equipment to meet whatever is the job at hand.

Dr. Bradner: In other words, the sum, the total of the requirements for the support system is really very extensive, and needs to be examined by people who are very aware of the requirements of any task.

Audience question: This question is directed to Dr. Weltman as regards to the post-dive heart rate increase. A couple of questions come to my mind in regard to this sub-question. No. 1, what was the temperature of the water at the time? No. 2, did you make body temperature measurements?

Dr. Weltman: The question is about the post-dive increase in heart rate — the temperature of the water — was, I think, in the low 60's — 61° or 62°, and no, we didn't make body temperature measurements but it depended on whether they were working with a heated suit. I think some of the measurements I showed you were even when they weren't working with the heated suits. I wouldn't expect body temperature to fall too much in that case.

The question that John brought up on fatigue, I think, is a very important one. With or without the heated suit, it was a taxing job and these divers were tired when they came out after their 50-minute work shift which was about an hour in the water and getting ready. Perhaps with getting ready and getting in the water, more like an hour and a half of dealing with this extremely heavy equipment on the deck during a hot day, sitting around in wet suits — you know — sweating and waiting around for everyone else to get ready. So you're looking at a pretty tired man when he gets on the ladder of the ship and is expected then to transport himself and about a 100 lbs. on his back, back to his seat. So, it's not remarkable that we saw heart rates like that. I think it's just something to remark and a rather dangerous situation.

Audience question: Why don't you at that point . . . just lift the diver out of the water?

Dr. Weltman: Good question. An excellent human factor observation. Why didn't they plan for an unloading rig for SEALAB III, where, in fact, you might have a diver in trouble who is still expected to make it up the ladder. Very cramped circumstances, very hard for somebody to reach down and lift him unless somebody is holding on to that second somebody's legs, very good point. I think the situation we're in now is that no one can point to a motivating or a motive force in this situation that requires these improvements to be made. In the diving industry, there's a fair amount of money being spent. I think people are making their money now with the existing situation. It's not immediately obvious how much more money you get if you improve the situation. *Many of us are in the scientific end of it and we would like to see things done because they're innately pleasing to us to have it done parsimoniously and nicely but there's nobody else whose livelihood depends on their being done correctly.*

Now, the aircraft industry, I think was in a different situation. If we can compare diving now with aircraft in its early stages. There, many commercial pressures arose — commercial and military — which speeded the development of the airplane. I don't see these same type of pressures working for diving. In the case of aerospace we manufactured the pressures artificially. You know, if the Russians hadn't done it, we would have had to invent them. Because — if not — we never would have got to the moon. Well, people are now tasting the after effects of artificial pressures. You know, we're still getting our fun out of our space walks but not as much as before. I don't know whether the seventh one is going to be nearly as much fun as the third, particularly when we realize what they cost. If somebody else can answer where the pressures are going to come from for improving the diving gear I would be most pleased.

Audience question: Aren't you glossing over many of the contribution factors that are observed when divers come out of the water?

Dr. Weltman: Oh, well, no doubt. I think . . . the question is that we're glossing over the many contributing factors that go into this reaction that we observe when divers come out of the water. No doubt. The point that I was trying to make is that there's rather a startling and sometimes neglected change and should certainly be taken account of in designing a diving system. The reasons for it are probably varied. I don't know whether temperature is as important as the hydrostatic effects, but you would certainly expect a little of both. As they enter, or as they come on to the ladder there's not a dramatic change in temperature condition but there certainly is a very dramaic change in their hydrostatic condition and a very dramatic change in the weight that they're expected to carry. They haven't been carrying any weight underwater. As heavy as their gear is, they're neutrally buoyant while they're working. All of a sudden it loses that neutral buoyancy and it's quite a shock. We have enough trouble standing up after we're been lying down in the heat, doing nothing. Here we're asking people to make the same type of adjustment when they haven't had to do any circulatory work while they were in the water and all of a sudden they have to do it again while they're on the deck. *We wouldn't let the astronauts go through that — let's put it that way.*

Audience question: Didn't the divers have to climb up a ladder to enter the SEALAB habitat?

Dr. Weltman: The question was whether or not in the SEALAB dive whether they'd be coming up a ladder and onto the deck. That's not so. The SEALAB habitat, you know — you can correct me — but as I remember the habitat, they had to come up a ladder to get into that first little cubicle where they would then have someone who migh help them take off the gear and store it. They could rest on a platform right underneath, but they would sill have to lift themselves up the ladder and onto the deck.

Audience question: Can you depend upon someone to assist the diver?

Dr. Weltman: Yeah, if you can depend on somebody being there. I would say, you know, again from a human factor standpoint the time that these things are the most important is when things start to go wrong and this is what in the aerospace they call fail-safe systems. I don't think enough attention has been paid to this type of philosophy in diving. Things are designed to go well, but if it goes wrong, it can go very wrong . . . as we demonstrated on, or as was, demonstrated on SEALAB.

Audience: May I make a response to that comment? We do not know whether it would eliminate that increase in heart rate. I'm asking and emphasizing that it needs to be measured and the mechanism by which the increased heart rate had manifested itself needs to be measured. You just can't rule it out because you think you can . . . air tanks down on the deck.

Audience question: What was the weight of the Mark VIII?

Mr. Quirk: I think the Mark VIII was 135 lbs. There's probably somebody rere who could verify that.

Dr. Weltman: It was about 140 lbs., I think. I underestimated at a 100 pounds.

Unidentified: Oh, no. It's way over.

Dr. Weltman: That's a fair pack.

Audience question: Dr. Bowen, I've heard that you have observed body core temperature drops of over 2° C.

Dr. Bowen: No, I haven't.

Audience question: Oh. you haven't?

Dr. Vaughn: I did. I'm sure they weren't comfortable. We weren't interested in that performance aspect. We were interested in whether or not they could continue to do the task that they'd been trained to do. 2° C. is about 3.6° F. and from the relatively high initial starting point, that kind of a drop is not clinically dangerous. I'm told that — I'm not sure of that. Mike might respond to that. Is that a clinical problem, a 2° C. drop? It is?

Dr. Bowen: I'd like to add one thing to that, if I may. Namely, that in performance terms the process of cooling is just as damaging, apparently, as being cold. Namely, the change of temperature especially as it's taking place in the periphery can be just as stressing, in terms of the performance test that I used, as actually being cold.

Audience question: What about the temperature drop in diver teams transported to the work site?

Dr. Vaughn. First of all they are sitting so they're not very active. There's not much work performance required so that the drain on body temperature is minimal. Secondly, the water flow problem is pretty much solved in that the vehicle has a loose fitting canopy. It has loose fitting canopies both fore and aft so that the people are essentially being transported through the water in a water slug at ambient pressure so that there's no flow over the body. They're currently wearing, I think, a fairly standard Farmer John wet suit, three-piece wet suit, quarter-inch jacket with a hood. There are a number of life support programs developing heated wet suits commercially within the Navy for this application, and there's also another level of standard wet suits that we could try — the Arctic brand of wet suits. We'll probably experiment with some of these models in June.

Dr. Bradner: Is it safe to say, though, that even with the kind of temperatures that we had here the diver probably would say "no sweat"?

Dr. Vaughn: I don't have . . . I don't think that . . . well, I don't know. It may be an adaptation level at this point, but I think that the divers that I work with are very sensible. I recall that when we first did the 4-hour runs, the subjects were a little apprehensive. They weren't sure what would happen over that long a period of time and neither were we. Our agreement or instructions were that if you felt any symptoms: dizziness, loss of orientation, any kind of symptom at all — go to the surface. We took, in the beginning, a great deal of safety precautions by starting one man at a time and replacing the second diver with a new diver at hour intervals and things of this kind. So, I don't think that that was an issue with us.

Dr. Bradner: Excuse me. This is of interest to me and I suspect that some of the audience, too. Let me see if I can paraphrase what I think you said. That for the 4-hour immersion in a capsule environment in contrast with even gentle swimming in water, which is running about say 60°, that the suit is not a severe limiting factor now.

Dr. Vaughn: Well, I think that, for the reasonably large body types — subcutaneous fat levels of, 15 to 20 cms I think is reasonable — that the Farmer John wet suits provide adequate protection in 60° water. Whether it will in colder water than that is unlikely. . . . Well, the point I was responding to was this tiger, gung-ho attitude as being a potential threat or a potential danger to the subject. My response is that I think people are more sensible than is generally bandied about when it comes to their survival.

Audience question: What if they report "no sweat" after a cold dive? I think your diver's giving you a snow job.

Dr. Vaughn: Well, none of our divers were interesting in doing that the next day, for example. They did not enjoy it. On the other hand, they would come out of the water even after the 6-hour exposure runs and take a cigarette out of the pack, a pack of matches and light the cigarette and. . . .

I think that they were very well habituated people. The group of seven had about 500 hours' bottom time by the time we were doing this.

Audience question: Well, from personal experience, I know this is not good as scientifically validated things, but I dove for about a year and a half up in Alaska in 38° and even 28° water and with 3/16th inch suits, and I found that the thickness in the hood and gloves much more important than the thickness of the suit. And I have no trouble whatsoever in 28° water when it's. . . .

Audience question: How long were you under?

Audience: As much as an hour doing hard work.

Dr. Vaughn: Well, it may have been that. . . .

Audience: I think the thickness of the suit is being overemphasized. I very much dislike thick suits.

Audience question: You want to say something about thick suits?

Dr. Bowen: Yes. I dislike thick suits, too. I think we all do. I think that probably the secret is doing hard work. You can't really talk about the level of cold stress being experienced unless you can quantify it in some way. One really needs some documentation of what the skin temperatures were, what your core temperature was, or some estimate of it. It's very difficult to get reliable estimate of core temperature. Incidentally, I used a very cheap way of doing it which was to make the men urinate immediately after they came out and measured the temperature of the urine which is the cheapest and easiest way of doing it. There are all kinds of very much more sophisticated techniques, obviously.

Dr. Bradner: Yes? We have time for about two more questions.

Audience question: This is for survival techniques. Some fliers were dropped in the North Atlantic. Originally the idea was that the fliers would struggle for long periods of time and generate metabolic heat to keep warm. However, it was found that they couldn't. They quickly exhausted their stores and succumbed from fatigue and drowned. They survived much better by just laying motionless in the water. Presumably, they had on a fine uniform and by remaining motionless, water didn't circulate through the suits. They were able to achieve somewhat a level of insulation.

Dr. Weltman: Wouldn't you say there's a difference, though, between short-term comfort and what would be maladaptive for long-term survival? If you know you're going to be in, for example, half an hour, an hour, and you can keep up the work level to that point, don't you think that because of the flow in your extremities, you'd be better able to maintain comfort and work than if you just tried to stay passive during certain parts of that time?

Audience question: There's no doubt about the situation in Dr. Egstrom's channel swimmers. Usually they're well padded and they can sustain high metabolic rates for very long periods of time.

The body's responses to cold water are to keep the core temperatures warm . . . they'll sacrifice extremities. The extremities can become very, very cold!

Dr. Weltman: Yeah, of course, the body doesn't know you're going to get a hot shower later.

Audience: I would like to add something I think it's been inferred. There's also been a couple of things left out. I emphasize my agreement with Dr. Sholing. He doesn't say how deep he dives. That makes a difference in the thickness of the suit he has at depth. He also mentions that he felt the hood, the gloves, and the boot fitting well was important. This is true. Without these things, the effect washes cold water under the suit. This would also have a factor. I think that until we can define all these things and measure them, we cannot make absolute statements.

Dr. Weltman: I think it's also a good example of just how attached we get to this equipment. I mean this recurs. I think I hit the point yesterday. I didn't do it today. People get so familiar with things and so proud of themselves for having mastered an entirely different type of thing . . . that changes are seen as not particularly worthwhile. I would think that we should be in a continual process of re-evaluating the equipment and its effect on work methodology. In a sense, the sport population does this more than the commercial population. Anytime some new configuration of fin comes out, it's a good seller for a while, while everybody tries it out. I think the places where you see the most resistance are really in the segments where they're doing their most useful work. It's a bit surprising to me. Some fields are like this and some fields aren't. Some fields will try something, anything new right away and some will be more resistant to technical innovation. I think diving is one of the fields that more are resistant to technical innovation. I don't think it has to be. Perhaps if what John said came through — that if the diver was actually given a channel of communication so that he knew that his ideas would be transmitted to the people who designed, and it resulted in real improvements — perhaps some of this resistance would be broken down and we would try new ways of doing things more readily.

Dr. Bradner: The session is adjourned.

Diving Behavior
Fourth Session

Speaker: **Dr. Arthur J. Bachrach, Director**
Behavioral Sciences Department
Naval Medical Research Institute
Bethesda, Maryland

Panelists: **Capt. Albert R. Behnke**
M. C., USN (Ret)
San Francisco, California

Michael Greenwood
Hawaii Laboratory
Naval Undersea Center
Kaneobe, Hawaii

Dr. Joseph B. MacInnes
Medical Director
Ocean Systems, Inc.
Toronto, Canada

Chairman: **Dr. Hugh Bradner**
Scripps Institution of Oceanography
La Jolla, California

Diving Behavior[1]

Arthur J. Bachrach
Naval Medical Research Institute
National Naval Medical Center
Bethesda, Maryland

The last few years have witnessed a significant rise in interest in the underwater world — a result of many factors, including the television exploits of Captain Cousteau, the growing recognition of the economic potential of the sea, and the pleasures of diving. While estimates of skin and scuba divers vary from *Time magazine's* guess several years back of eight million skin and one million scuba divers to more conservative estimates (Los Angeles County's diving program estimated about 200,000 divers in that area in 1968, and Los Angeles is a major center), it is true that skin and scuba diving have become popularized to a large degree. With this increase in popularity, the problems attendant upon diving have also increased, perhaps exponentially.

The sources of the problems in diving are many and complex. Equipment and training concepts have not always kept up with the growing technologies of engineering and learning theory and, in characteristic fashion, the enthusiasm arising from newly discovered thrills is not always tempered with reason or reality. A recent issue of *Holiday* magazine devoted a number of articles as well as the cover to skin and scuba diving. In one paper entitled "The Ruins Under the Sea," archeologist George F. Bass described the pleasures of marine archeology. The subhead, under the title, (undoubtedly the product of an editorial aide and not Dr. Bass) adds a disturbing note: It reads "The last earthly frontier left to explore is the ocean floor — and anyone can do it."

[1] The opinions and statements contained herein are the private ones of the writer and are not to be construed as official or reflecting the views of the Navy Department or the naval service at large.

I'm firmly convinced that not everyone can do it and those who can might be trained and equipped better to do it. An inevitable part of standard books on diving are the hazards enumerated (such as air embolism and decompression problems), yet we must take a closer look at how effective such warnings are in view of the behaviors observed and inferred in diving accidents.

I wish there were a diving term comparable to that used to describe the skier as "an object hurtling through space." An article on ski injuries some years ago referred to "the ballistics of skiing" and analyzed the skier as an object traveling at a certain speed and momentum and therefore suitable for analysis of effects of impact when this object (the skier) collided with another object (the tree). A term such as "the biophysics of diving" hardly carries the metacommunication of this colorful description.

There are many thoughtful reviews of diving hazards and diving accidents (Duffner, 1961; Parker, 1965; Denney & Read, 1965; Webster, 1966; Taylor, *et al,* 1963; Waller, *et al,* 1964, Lanphier & Gillen, 1963), as well as detailed descriptions of accidents (cf. Strauss & Wright, 1969; Seemann & Wandel, 1967). I hope to sketch out some information and inferences on diving hazards as a basis for discussion of the diving factors of health, equipment, and training.

DIVING ACCIDENTS

Hazards and Statistics

Webster's review of national statistics on diving fatalities (1966) reported a tally of 86 diving deaths in the United States in 1965 with coastal states accounting for around a half (California, 21; Florida, 19). Los Angeles County, a major diving area, shows a tally of around 68 diving fatalities in the greater Los Angeles area from 1954-1968. Given the large number of persons actively engaged in diving, perhaps such figures might be considered statistically insignificant — but no death is insignificant, especially in a sport that is both popular and hazardous.

It may be of interest to compare scuba diving with other high-risk sports, particularly the popular skiing and skydiving. Ski fatalities are estimated to run around five a year, mostly as a result of bad conditions on slopes. Interestingly enough, skiers who get killed in accidents are not usually recreational skiers but are working skiers out testing slopes. Accidents among skydivers are not generally separated from other fatal parachute accidents — voluntary jumps are recreational while involuntary jumps are a result of aircraft difficulties. In recent years, general aviation parachute incident fatalities ranged from 10 in 1963 to 30 in 1967.* Even if we do not allow for a fair percentage of these fatalities being involuntary jumps, the total is less than those incurred in skin and scuba diving. A better comparison is between diving and skiing in view of the probable similarity in the

* Ten of these 30 fatalities occurred in one major tragedy in Lake Erie near Huron, Ohio, on August 27, 1967.

numbers of those engaged in these sports; certainly in both cases the number of fatalities is much higher than in skydiving. Comparing the reported average of five deaths a year on the ski slopes with the large number of diving accidents, the latter appears much more hazardous.

Webster's review (1966) of American fatalities (reported in newspapers) occurring in U. S. or foreign waters during 1965, identified 86 deaths. Of the total 86, 26 accidents were in skin diving, 60 in scuba. The majority were male victims (24 skin diving and 58 scuba). Age distribution for the skin diving fatalities was 11-49 years, with a peak of 21-25; for scuba, it was a range of 14-59 years, peaking at 16-20. Los Angeles County data show a similar trend — most victims have been males between 16-25 years. Apparently young divers are the primary accident group in skin and scuba diving facilities.

Webster (1966) adds a most interesting note to these statistics, reporting that many of the young victims were experienced and "unusually skilled" swimmers. Some were members of swimming teams and, in one instance, the victim was a state champion swimmer. This is a provocative datum to consider with regard to the types of skills important in diving. While we have assumed that swimming competence is a necessity in diving, its relevance might be more closely evaluated — it is possible that swimming experience might lead an inexperienced diver to overestimate his ability and to assume risks ordinarily not taken. This is purely conjecture, but nonetheless, is an interesting finding and one worth studying.

Formal Training

The role of diving experience itself needs analysis. Denney and Read (1965) indicate in their analysis of 21 deaths associated with scuba diving in Michigan, that 15 of the 21 fatalities occurred to inexperienced divers. Only 6 of the 21 had formal diving training with greater than two years' experience and, of the remaining 15 inexperienced divers, three were receiving instruction at the time of their accident and another three died on their first attempt at diving.

Webster (1966) found in his analysis of newspaper stories that when the experience of the diver was mentioned, in 33 cases, experienced divers totalled 17 of the drowning victims, inexperienced divers comprised the remaining 16. Allowing for the subjective and sometimes inaccurate assessment of newspaper reporters regarding experience in diving, 17 of the 86 deaths occurred to divers assumed to have experience. The statistics are very shaky in view of the *post hoc* nature of data gathering and reliance on newspaper reports, but the percentages presented by Denney and Read for the Michigan series and Webster's national figures are comparable: 15/21 inexperienced for the former, 69/86 for the latter. These data are similar to those reported by Los Angeles County where lack of previous training in diving appeared in the majority of fatalities.

In Denney and Read's (1965) report of 21 deaths associated with SCUBA diving in Michigan during the years 1959-1965 they found that

18 victims were diving in water 25 feet deep or less. Other depths were around 33′, 45′, and 270′, but the overwhelming majority of accidents occurred in shallow water.

Webster (1966) reported exhaustion (often related to panic) was the assumed proximate cause in 46 of the 86 deaths, with the next largest number (16) inferred to be a result of entrapment or entanglement under ice, in kelp, underwater ledges, or various lines. Denney and Read (1965) also reported that 5 of the 21 Michigan fatalities were lost under ice (4) and one in thick weeds. A large number of deaths reported in both surveys occurred to divers swimming alone or who had become separated from fellow divers. The buddy system, long held sacred by diving instructors, may need further reinforcement.

The question of panic occurs throughout the accounts of the diving accidents, panic that seems to override certain aspects of training even in divers who have had formal instruction. For example, it has been reported that in all of the deaths attributed to diving in California the diver was found still wearing his weight belt despite the attempts in diving courses to make jettisoning of the weight belt automatic in emergencies. The death of a young woman in Tucson a couple of years ago is illustrative. This woman, enrolled in a diving course but lacking experience, was reported to have surfaced in panic and drowned while diving for golf balls in a twelve-foot trap in dark water. When her body was recovered, she was wearing her weight belt, and in addition, was still clutching a heavy bag of golf balls.

Equipment problems were implicated in 23 of the 86 cases Webster (1966) reported. In these cases the victim lacked a knife with which to free himself from possible entanglement, had an inoperable life vest or ill-fitting face mask, or substandard and defective valves and regulators. Yet equipment handling is also a major feature of diver training. The frequency of misuse of equipment reported in accidents suggests that the training had not sufficiently emphasized the proper use of gear or, more likely, that the inexperience of the diver, coupled with the easy availability of apparatus (without necessary instruction in its use) in dive shops in certain sections of the country may be the crucial problems. As far as location goes, about half of Webster's (1966) reported fatalities were in ocean, bay, or other large bodies of water, with the next largest numbers occurring in such areas as lakes, ponds, quarries, and caves.

Another interesting conclusion can be drawn: virtually all of the accidents occurring to sports divers happen to civilians. Denney and Read (1965) reported that in 1962 eight out of ten serious diving casualties treated in U. S. Navy recompression chambers were civilian rather than military. Los Angeles County data show 14 non-fatal diving accidents in 1966-1968, most of which were treated at the Long Beach Naval recompression facility.

Physiological Factors

Decompression. Many accidents and deaths occurred in shallow water. Thus, in this series, the major threat of decompression sickness about which so much teaching occurs in diving courses, seems ruled out as a significant diving accident feature in as much as the likelihood of deep, long dives is rather low.

There remains, however, the problem of repetitive dives and decompression, the importance of which I would certainly not underestimate. Divers going into even relatively shallow water on repetitive dives may build up a cumulative effect that makes the threat of decompression sickness a real one. Nevertheless, I believe that the problems of hyperventilation and overdistension of the scuba diver's lungs should receive more emphasis in the diving training program.

Hyperventilation/overdistension of lungs. Air is compressed under increased pressure, while water is not. This physical fact is extremely important to the diver as his lungs constitute air-filled cavities. For example, as the free diver descends into the water the pressure on his body increases so that at a depth of 33 feet the pressure is twice that of sea level. On the surface the pressure is 14.8 psi (or one atmosphere); it is doubled at 33 feet, or two atmospheres. The air cavities, such as the lungs, are compressed on descent. However, if a diver breathing compressed air fills his lungs and ascends without exhaling any of the air, the decreased pressure on ascent will result in the doubling of gas volume in the lungs as he hits the surface. The examples above involve a basic law of physics (Boyle's Law, as well as Henry's Law, and Dalton's Law) which constitutes a major focus of our attention in diving accidents.

Pulmonary Barotrauma

Denney and Read (1965) observed with regard to the increased lung volume during diver ascent . . . "any interference with expiration prevents release of this increased volume and thus produces acute pulmonary emphysema. The resultant barotrauma has been shown to cause extensive damage to the alveolar wall." In a majority of the 21 deaths in the Michigan study (11 cases) the symptoms observed were "stupor, decerebrate rigidity, convulsions, and hemoptysis, all occurring shortly after surfacing." These signs, as Denney and Read indicate, suggest "pulmonary barotrauma and air embolism to the brain as the mechanism of injury." Such accidents are often mistaken for the bends but, as noted above, few divers go deep enough or stay long enough to run a serious risk of decompression sickness. To be sure, decompression sickness occurs in sports divers and is a hazard, but I believe a greater risk is air embolism, and a closely related diving problem — hyperventilation, associated with panic or anxiety in the water.

Physiological consequences of hyperventilation are many and marked. Breathing normally maintains a balance between CO_2 and O_2. Rising CO_2 levels (or falling O_2 levels) trigger respiratory activity. (Hyperventilation can drop the CO_2 level dangerously low, while O_2 levels remain unchanged. This drop, if maintained as in a state of panic, has profound effects on the human respiratory metabolism.) According to the *U. S. Navy Diving Manual,* hyperventilation can induce a, muscular spasms, loss of consciousness, and end result." Another danger resulting from hyper- panic is spasmic tetanic closure of the glottis mani- voluntary control. If this occurs on ascent in a compressed air, the rapid increase in intrathoracic ult in rupture of the alveolar membrane of the lung and sm. Seaman and Wandel (1969) report that water around the outh in a diver who is experiencing discomfort may lead to a "cramp-like attempt to hold air" leading further to "a closure of the glottis which can prevent all escape of the expanding lung air."

Neurological and Behavioral Factors

Anxiety/Panic. There are also potential neurological changes associated with hyperventilation. Stein, Roth, and Simonova (1967) report electroencephalographic (EEG) changes (generally changes in the alpha rhythm), that are associated with hyperventilation in normal adults. Reports of weakness, numbness, "tingling," and impaired vision are among the neuropsychological events found with hyperventilation. A behavioral problem occurs in a cyclical fashion. Anxiety may occasion hyperventilation, leading to physical symptoms (such as dizziness) which may occur, inducing further anxiety and panic with hyperventilation. The possibility that loss of consciousness from overbreathing may induce relaxation on the glottis, a counter-problem of the one discussed previously, is a related danger. Thus the airway may flood and drowning result. Prasser (1969) believes that drowning from hyperventilation associated with panic is "likely an unrecognized and not uncommon form of death."

I have mentioned the problem of panic as significant in the diving accidents. In his book *Go To The Widow Maker,* James Jones, writing of scuba diving says ". . . and panic, *panic* was the biggest danger, enemy, the *only* danger that there was in diving."

There is not enough known about the incidence, nature, and timing of panic in divers. Do experienced and inexperienced divers both panic at times? If so, under what conditions? Is anxiety about a particular dive a normal part of every diver's experience? Such questions may arise in part from an evaluation of anxiety situations in other hazardous sports (e.g., studies reported by Fenz and Epstein in 1969 on skydivers, experienced and novice). Anxiety was found in both groups but peaked earlier in the experienced group. If an experienced skydiver decided not to jump, the decision was made early in the day. "Once the commitment to jump is made, fear declines." On the other hand, the anxiety peaked about the time of a jump in the inexperienced skydivers. Perhaps some similar kinds of data might be obtained on experienced and novice skin the scuba divers.

Anxiety, properly controlled, is a normal event and indeed has positive features of increasing the individual's sensitivity to problems and procedures of a dive. The diver properly in control — which also means with proper equipment — is assumed to be able to handle himself in an emergency. Overwhelming anxiety, disabling an individual, is what is generally referred to as "panic." Defense against overwhelming anxiety appears to be largely a function of the person's confidence in his own control and his capability to cope. Panic, loosely defined, is a strong, fearful perception by an individual that he is out of control, that he is not capable of coping with the situation in which he finds himself, leading to behaviors that not only do not solve the problem posed by the danger but actually may work directly against such solution. Jones, in the novel referred to above, depicts a danger situation and loss of control where the diver is in a narrow underwater cave:

> But when he was in far enough that he could no longer bend his knees to flutter his feet, the panicky breathlessness, the sensation of being unable to breathe, to get enough air, which panic brings . . . hit him debilitatively. Stopping, he forced himself to breathe deeply but it didn't help. Suddenly his instinct was to throw off everything and run for the surface blindly, even though covered by coral rock, get to anywhere where there was air. Instead he reached out with his hands and pulled himself further in, trying to keep his movements slow and liquid, unviolent, though by now he didn't care whether the coral cut him or not.

Panic not only interferes with coping behavior and the diver's behavior, but may narrow perception (Weltman & Egstrom, 1966) and create, as Jones says, "blind" rushing toward leaving the emergency.

Such debilitating behavior also occasions a lack of awareness of the factors in impending disaster and a failure to take necessary corrective action.

Summary of Accident Factors

Let us, at this point, review what the above discussion has covered. Diving accidents leading to fatalities occur, for the most part, in young, inexperienced divers at relatively shallow depths. Problems of equipment and its proper use contribute to the hazard, as does the ignorance of standard diving safety rules (such as diving with a buddy). A major cause of death with scuba, often mistaken for decompression sickness, appears to be pulmonary and brain damage occurring as a result of improper exhalation of air upon ascent. Panic in the inexperienced diver in an emergency situation probably has psychological consequences of further reducing problem-solving behavior as well as physiological consequences such as glottal stricture, which may contribute further to the inability to exhale lung air. Another dangerous physiological consequence of panic and attendant hyperventilation is potential loss of consciousness. It is also likely that "instinctively" in a water situation the inexperienced diver, especially in an emergency, conserves air in fear that he will run out of lung air before he can surface. All of these events contribute to the likelihood of air embolism.

Much of the discussion so far has centered on the assumption that the major accidents occur during *ascent.* It is also true, of course, that problems of pressure equalization on descent can produce "squeeze" in the air cavities of the diver (cf. Strauss & Wright, 1969) and that such hazards as O_2 toxicity, CO_2 or nitrogen intoxication, and dangerous marine animals can be found on the bottom as well as on ascent or descent. However, the data appear to support the position that ascent remains the single most dangerous period of the dive (Lanphier, 1969).

Let us now turn to the consideration of factors in the behavior of the diver that can prepare him best for the sport of diving. These factors will be discussed under the rubrics of *diver health, diving equipment* and *diver training.* The primary emphasis will be on the latter.

DIVER BEHAVIOR

While statistics are not readily available, it appears that few diving courses require a thorough physical examination. Indeed, some courses require none at all. It is important that the guidelines for medical examination be rigidly followed as delineated in the U. S. Navy *Diving Manual,* (1970) and *The New Science of Skin and Scuba Diving,* (1968) prepared by the Council for National Cooperation in Aquatics. In particular, examination should include attention to possible signs of lung problems such as emphysema. A diver in good physical condition should also have stamina to prevent the danger of exhaustion, so critical a problem in diving accidents.

The physical condition of the diver with respect to weight, (not entirely agreed upon by diving medical personnel) seems to point to overweight as a possible health hazard from the standpoint of lowered stamina and physical exhaustion, the potential risk to heart, and its possible relationship to fat metabolism. With regard to the latter, Behnke (1969) and Pauley and Cockett (1970) have pointed to the similarities that exist between fat embolism and decompression sickness, suggesting that the explanation of decompression sickness entirely in terms of nitrogen bubbles in the blood stream is incomplete, and that lipid metabolism and liver functioning need careful study.

Another aspect of diver health that needs consideration is that psychological condition of the diver. Here, I am sorry to say, there are no clear guidelines. Psychological tests are not very effective predictive devices in general, and we psychologists have a great deal to be modest about. One meaningful way to screen psychological condition is by assessing the stress response of the beginning diver in his training situation — actuarial data on performance are the best criteria for predicting success. As Aquadro (1965) observes, psychological and psychiatric assessment of submarine candidates did not prove too valuable but "the best predictor of these ultimate criteria (of success) seems to be early performance in the submarine training program." It would be very helpful if it were possible to have measures of stress in beginning divers such as heart rate and respiration rate. Weltman and Egstrom (1966), Callaway and Dembo (1958), report on the perceptual narrowing that occurs in novice divers presumed to be under stress which may be observed by training personnel. The instructor should develop a set of discriminating observations in the early periods of training that will pinpoint problems and strengths in the student diver. But here we have a problem: Many a cool pool diver becomes stressed in his first open sea dive. This problem, which we will discuss in more detail under Diver Training, is one that relates to the conditions under which training occurs.

A diver in good physical and psychological shape, competent to handle himself in various diving situations, is a safer diver.

Diving Equipment

As noted earlier, Webster (1966) indicates that in 23 of the 86 fatalities, faulty equipment or the lack of appropriate equipment (such as a diving knife to escape entanglement) were implicated. Standardization of equipment, the careful fitting of equipment to the individual diver, and proper maintenance are basic. Parker (1965) offers a guideline to the features that good, safe equipment should have:

Mask: cover the eyes and nose only, fit comfortably and make a good seal, shatterproof glass, steel retaining band to keep face plate in place.

Fins: fit comfortably, be either full foot or permanent strap (adjustable straps are unreliable).

Snorkel: rubber or flexible plastic with rubber mouthpiece, straight "J" tube shape. No ball or valve of any description.

Tank: government approved (i.e., pressure tested), safety manual reserve valve ("J" valve), use compressed, filtered air only.

Regulator: good quality, single or double stage, recognized brand name product.

Straps: all straps, harnesses, etc., should be of the quick release type.

In addition, the evaluation of facilities where divers obtain air fills for their tanks is crucial. Bad air, perhaps containing oil or other pollutants from the environment, or a faulty compressor can be a major hazard for the diver. State certification of air quality and equipment standards for fill stations (such as that adopted by New Jersey in 1964) appears to be a meaningful public health measure.

Diver Training

We come now to the most important aspect of diver behavior — at least from my own point of view — the training of the diver. Considerable thought and planning have gone into diver training by such groups as the National Association of Underwater Instructors and the Los Angeles County Underwater Instructors Association, but I would like to review some possible applications of behavior technology and learning theory to the all-important problem of diver education.

In recent years a technology of behavior has emerged that delineates principles of behavior and their application to training which may lead to more effective educational procedures. This technology is an experimental analysis of behavior (Skinner, 1953) in which the analysis of the conditions under which behavior is established and maintained becomes a major focus. The term used to describe the establishment of behavior is *shaping,* based on the principle that the way behavior is developed is by successive approximations leading toward a specified terminal behavior. In other words, the trainer must define the particular behavior he wishes to establish and then select the increments of shaping by which he will gradually develop this behavior.

To illustrate, using a diving example, much of what is called *training* in diving is actually an *examination.* Can the trainee dive down to the bottom of a 25′ tank and clear his mask? This is the terminal behavior desired but instead of staging the steps leading to this goal, diving training most often moves directly to the end point. It might be more efficient to approximate the behaviors successively by, let us say, practice on the surface clearing the mask with the face just under the water, than at 5′ while standing, gradually developing the skill until the clearing at 25′ is a development of the skill and not a premature examination of it. An analogue might be the incremental stages leading to high pole-vaulting.

The use of terminal behaviors as an examination is, in essence, a "disputed passage" through which the individual must pass before he can move on to the *next* disputed passage. Shaping is a major method of the proper establishment of desired behaviors. It is an approach to behavior in which a potential for responding is assumed. It is the responsibility of the experimenter (or instructor) to sculpt, from the raw materials of the individual's response patterning, that combination of responses which add up to a chain of behaviors usually referred to as a "skill." The first responsibility of the experimenter in shaping behavior is to identify the responses specifically that he wishes to shape — not in a vague and abstract fashion, but rather to delineate clearly those motor responses desired. This, for example, may involve a combination of behaviors such as is found in the general response of clearing a mask. Properly to identify the behaviors involved the instructor must be aware of such elements as postural positions and the angle of the diver in the water. If he is going to teach these responses he must make himself clearly aware of the elements of the skill.

The next critical aspect of shaping behavior is properly to sequence the chain of responses. The term "successive approximation" previously used illustrates this. In addition to identifying the elements of the response the experimenter must identify the terminal behavior he wishes, that is, what he wishes the individual to be doing at a particular point in time. The consummate behavior or skill can then be broken up into subelements which are sequentially shaped. Critical in this is the appropriate use of cues and rewards (or in experimental analysis of behavior terms, stimuli and reinforcements).

Beginning with the mass of responses available to the individual to be shaped, the experimenter reinforces successively closer approximations to the terminal response which he wishes the student to have. To use an animal example, (as psychologists are so fond of doing) let us take a rat whom we wish to train to press a bar in a box in order to obtain food. When the training starts the rat is first trained to get his food from a hopper placed on one wall of the experimental box. After he has developed this response to approach the box to get his food and his free reinforcements by such feedings, the food no longer appears in the hopper. The experimenter now (through some device such as a solenoid-operated switch) hand controls delivery of a pellet of food. At first the requirement is simply that the animal face the lever placed close to the food hopper, then with increasing demands for complexity the rat is required to approach, touch, and ultimately to press the lever with sufficient force to operate it. Once this is accomplished the rat can feed himself and the delivery of food can now be made contingent upon other behaviors, such as having the rat respond to a stimulus light. On such basic responses can complex chain behaviors be built. An example of such a complex chain behavior built upon a simple feeding response is seen in the example of Rodent E. Lee.*

A rat who worked with me at the University of Virginia named Rodent E. Lee was reinforced for pressing a bar to feed himself. He was then placed in a large experimental box with a number of specific tasks to be done in sequence. The idea for Rodent's box was based upon similar work done a number of years ago by a team of psychologists, Rosemary Pierrel and J. Gilmour Sherman. The demonstrations indicate that complex behavior may be conditioned response-by-response to form a final "fluid" chain of responses. Clearly Rodent E. Lee is reinforced by the presentation of food in the hopper following his response of pressing the lever, but before he can get to press the bar to receive his food reinforcement Rodent has to climb a spiral staircase, pass a drawbridge, climb a ladder, enter a cable car to pull himself across a gap a couple of feet above the floor of the box, climb another stairway, hit two keys on the toy piano which operate a microswitch, enter a model railroad crossing gate (which has been opened by the microswitch on the piano), run through the tunnel when the crossing gate is opened, climb into an elevator, then pull

---

* At this point a film of complex chaining illustrating Rodent E. Lee's behavior was shown to the conference.

a chain to release the elevator. He rides to the bottom floor in the elevator and presses his bar to receive his pellets. This response chain is demonstrated in Figures 1 through 10 (Bachrach, 1964).

This experiment was not set up as a demonstration purely for amusement (although the behavior of Rodent E. Lee is extremely reinforcing to the experimenter) but rather to show that at each particular stage the behavior of the organism is conditioned specifically. By watching Rodent run through these paces (which he does in about 15 seconds) the impression is given that this is a fluid single motion, but, of course, he was not trained that way. For one thing he was trained "backwards;" that is, he was trained first to approach the tray where the food was, to press the bar to deliver the pellet, then he was shaped to ride the elevator to get down to the lever to receive the pellet. Next he was shaped to pull the chain which released the elevator so that he could ride down to the bottom floor, and so on. At each individual step of the shaping the response desired by the experimenter was achieved by approximation techniques. As an example, the most difficult response of getting him to pull the chain to release the elevator was accomplished by successive approximation, i.e., by getting him to make movements toward the chain, to sniff it,

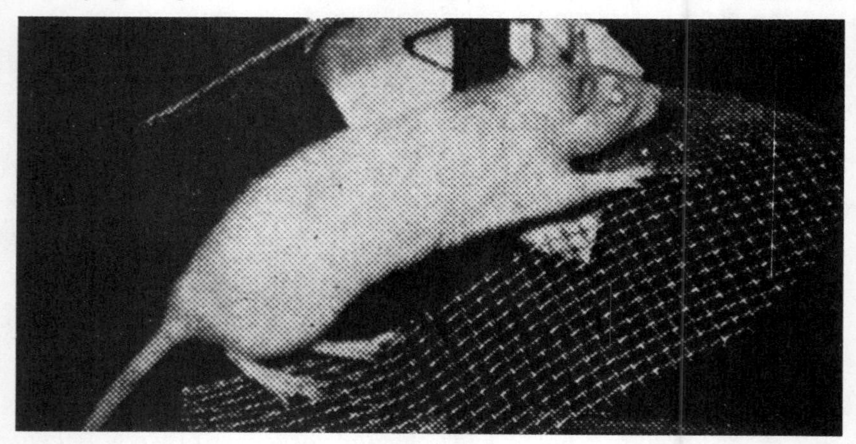

Figure 1

Figure 2

Figure 3

Figure 4

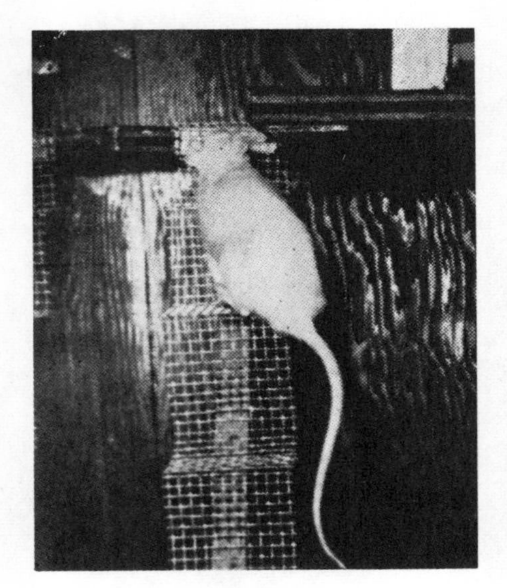

Figure 5

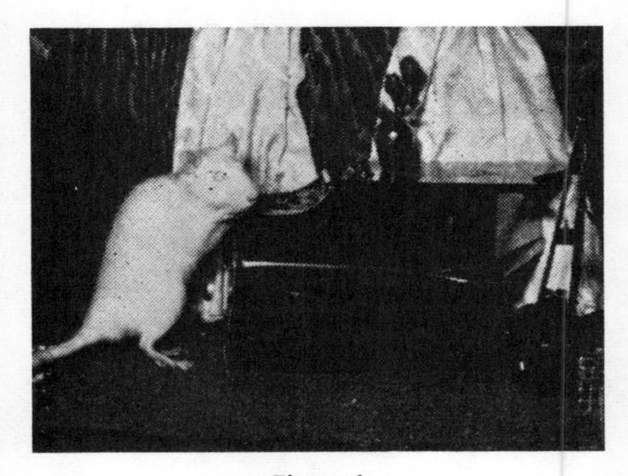

Figure 6

Figure 7

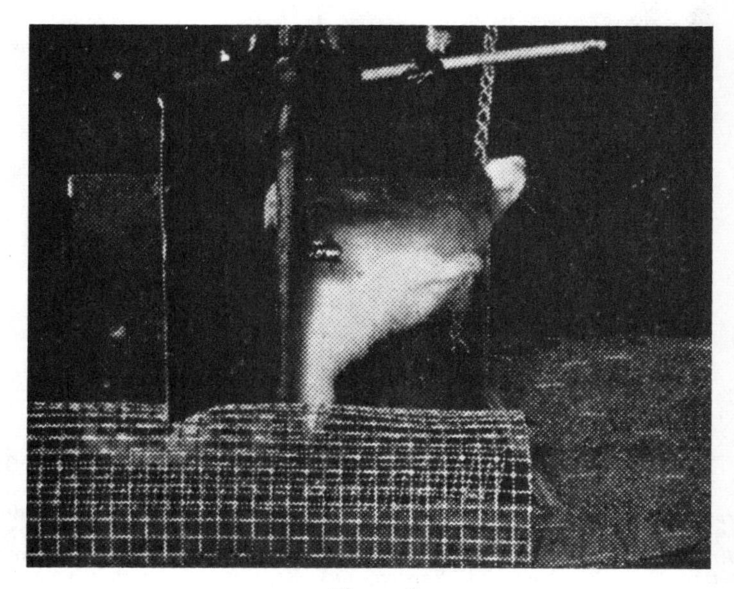

Figure 8

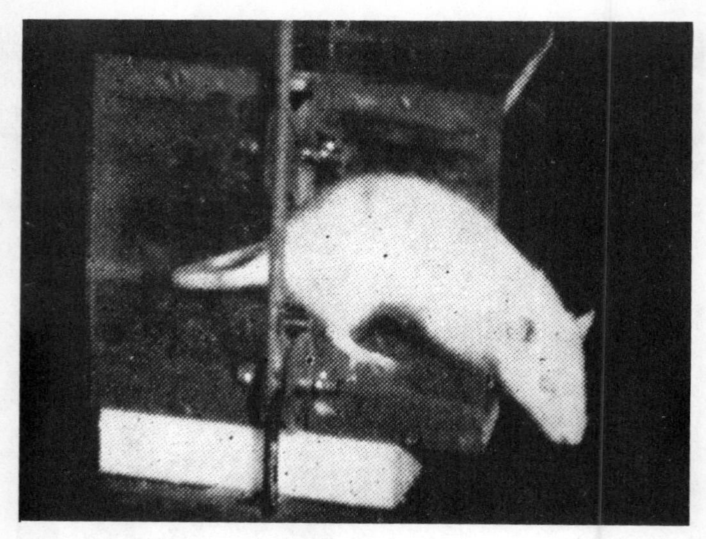

Figure 9

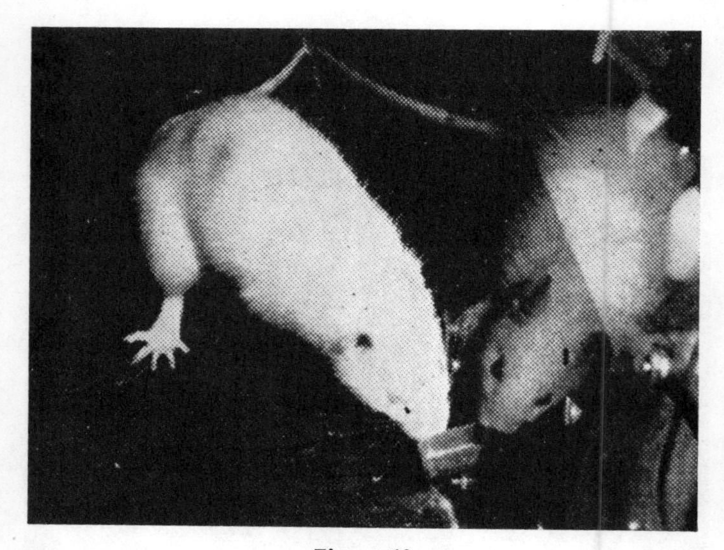

Figure 10

to touch it with his nose and his paws, and finally, to pull it. Each one of these responses was an approximation toward the terminal behavior of pulling the chain.

An obvious advantage of training backward is that each response becomes not only a cue (or discriminative stimulus) for the immediate and succeeding response, but it is also a reinforcement for the one that preceded the response. Pressing the piano key, for example, sets the occasion for a click which is associated with the opening of the crossing gate, making the tunnel accessible to running through to reach the elevator.

Not all "skills" such as those Rodent E. Lee demonstrated can readily be trained backwards. Most (certainly diving) should proceed in general as a chain of increasing complexity (with appropriate cues and rewards programmed — again in opposition to the "disputed passage") leading chronologically to orchestration of equipment and personal talents in the water. Some athletic skills in humans might possibly be trained backwards such as, for example, golf strokes where the follow-through might be the first postural response to be conditioned, but whether the shaping is done on a chronological or backwards order the principles remain the same: the specific responses demanded of the learner must be specified and identified, shaping must proceed sequentially and logically in terms of increasing complexity with sucessive approximation toward a terminal behavior, and appropriate rewards and cues must be programmed in logically.

We know that behavior is best maintained under conditions similar to those under which it was established. Here we invoke the principle of *generalization* which means that a response shaped under Condition A can be expected to occur in Condition B, given similarities between the two. The problem so often encountered in training is that the generalization is at best difficult as, for example, in the problem of transferring diving behavior from the relatively safe, protected, enclosed swimming pool to the open sea. To ask a diver to leap into the open water from a boat on a checkout dive after all his diving experience has been in a closed pool has the obvious advantage of evaluation under real diving conditions. It may also be a disputed passage, however, inasmuch as the stimulus conditions are different to a large degree. The skills in equipment use, *et cetera,* may be similar, but the environmental conditions are not. It is suggested that the same may apply to the open sea diver who tries cave diving for the first time. Generalization from open water experience to enclosed cave diving may be incomplete.

RECOMMENDATIONS

We offer for consideration a training program, again based on successive approximation toward the terminal behavior, in which the pool training (with the major emphasis on equipment use) is followed not by on open sea checkout dive but by a transition to movement into the sea from the surf or, perhaps, from a shallow cove where the diver trainee can generalize pool experience gradually in an open but still protected environment. The shaping of the behavior in this way develops increasing skill and concomitant confidence in handling self and equipment in a growing complexity of requirements.

The open sea checkout dive washes out some divers and, while this may be good in weeding out potentially poor divers in a true stress situation, it has the disadvantage of possibly screening out divers who, with proper training, could eventually reach a good level of proficiency. It is unfair and uneconomical to allow disputed passage training approaches to function as a selection system. The proper scheduling of training stages is the best diagnostic device available to predict future performance. Accordingly, shaping is also assessment in telling the trainer and trainee at what points poor performance occurs.

Overdistension

A most critical behavior, related to the accident problem, is the proper use of exhalation upon ascent. As we have seen, overdistension of the lungs is a major diving hazard. It is crucial to devote more meaningful time in sports diving courses to the hazards of hyperventilation, air embolism, and related problems. While this is a part of standard diving training, I feel it is not given sufficient emphasis. So often standard diving training concentrates heavily on decompression problems and the use of dive tables which is more important to the deep diver, the one who, in such systems as the University of California program, is specifically qualified for various depths. In such a program a qualification card may specify a 25′ or a 200′ diver. I feel that the emphasis in early training should be on the hazards of air embolism and that the concentration on decompression sickness be less in the beginning training and more detailed in the advanced training. Perhaps it is similar to learning anatomy in medical school; a briefing to be basically grounded in anatomy is essential for all students but the physician who is to specialize in surgery must relearn, in great detail, anatomical data when he is ready to proceed to deeper application. The beginning diver should be acquainted with problems and hazards of decompression; but, in view of the overwhelming number of accidents above two atmospheres, detailed handling of such tools as repetitive dive tables might best be part of the surgical anatomy. As part of the basic training, as is done in such programs as the University of California program, it is crucial that training in controlled, emergency ascent be included. The proper control of respiration in ascent and descent (which necessitates knowing and experiencing proper exhalation techniques under controlled conditions) is perhaps the most important skill to be established in the diver.

The problem of panic has been touched upon several times, from both a psychological and physiological standpoint. Training, using shaping techniques, might also be addressed to this hazard of diving. Panic occurs in situations where the subject, as we have noted, fears loss of control. Shaping of competence in handling emergencies is possible, not by lectures on how to cope but with successive exposure, under controlled conditions, to emergency situations in which the trainee can develop gradual skills in coping. It is not accurate to talk about self-confidence in terms other than shaping by successful completion of tasks under conditions similar to emergency events.

There is another aspect to this that may be limned, drawing upon the clinical literature. Anxiety responses, under careful shaping, can be neutralized by the establishment of responses incompatible with anxiety (Wolpe, 1958, 1962; Bachrach, 1964). Perhaps some approach to using this concept in training might be fruitful. I feel that not enough of the usual training course involves what the diver can *do* underwater. Proper emphasis on equipment and its use and maintenance occupies a good deal of the course, with an occasional nod at marine biology, also frequently couched in hazardous terms — the animals to avoid. One response incompatible with anxiety is *purposeful work* and it would be worth studying the effects on trainee discomfort in the water of having specific training in underwater work such as photography, marine biology, shell-collecting, or underwater archeology, to name a few examples. This would, I believe, accomplish several purposes: it would maintain an interest in the water as a goal other than mere entry and would keep the diver from over-concern about his gear (the constant checking of gauges, for example). It would also provide a future-oriented dive in terms of products captured, photographed, and unearthed.

There are, of course, a great many diving instructors who work at these ideas and much of what I have suggested is in use. Glen Egstrom at UCLA has been a major influence on shaping diving instruction. Len Greenstone of Los Angeles, for example, has diver trainees accomplish work tasks underwater which he feels keeps them too busy to worry about gear unduly. Jim Stewart at Scripps takes a somewhat different and provocative task in establishing a response incompatible with anxiety. He has trainees sitting at the bottom of a dull pier area where there is nothing to see or do and feels that the irritation and the boredom damps out anxiety. Skilled diver instructors such as these are in a better position than I to evaluate training programs. My purpose in reviewing some of the possible applications of an experimental analysis of behavior to diver training is done with appropriate humility.

The behavior of divers is a most fascinating area. Our goal as divers, educators, and researchers is to improve knowledge and application of physiology and training to a point where divers can dive safely and efficiently for work and for pleasure.

REFERENCES

Aquadro, C. F. Examination and selection of personnel for work in an underwater environment. *Journal of Occupational Medicine,* 1965, *7,* 619-625.

Bachrach, A. J. Some applications of operant conditioning to behavior therapy.

In J. Wolpe, A. Salter, and L. J. Reyna, (Eds.) *The conditioning therapies: The challenge in psychotherapy.* New York: Holt, Rinehart & Winston, 1964.

Behnke, A. R. Some projections in the field of hyperbaric medicine. Lecture to Naval Medical Research Institute, 6 November 1969.

Berkum, M. M. Performance decrement under psychological stress. *Human Factors,* 1964, *6,* 21-30.

Callaway, E., III, & Dembo, D. Narrowed attention: A psychological phenomenon that accompanies a certain physiological change. *AMA Archives Neurological Psychiatry,* 1958, *79,* 74-90.

Council for National Co-Operation in Aquatics, *The new science of skin and scuba diving.* (3rd ed.) New York: Association Press, 1968.

County of Los Angeles, Department of Parks and Recreation Underwater Unit, Underwater Instructor Workshop Training Supplement on Diving Accident Statistics, 1968.

Davis, G. D. A review of skin diving hazards. *Medical Journal of Australia,* February 10, 1968, 230-235.

Denney, M. K. & Read, C. Scuba-diving deaths in Michigan. *Journal of American Medical Association,* 1965, *192,* 120-122.

Duffner, G. J. Scuba diving injuries: Predisposing causes and prevention. *Journal of American Medical Association,* 1961, *175,* 375-378.

Ernsting, J. *Some effects of raised intrapulmonary pressure in man.* The Advisory Group for Aerospace Research and Development of NATO. Maidenhead, England: Technivision, Ltd., 1966.

Fenz, W. D. & Epstein, S. Stress in the Air. *Psychology Today,* September 1969.

Jones, J. *Go to the widow maker.* New York: Dell Publishing, 1968.

Lanphier, E. H. Pulmonary function. In P. B. Bennett & D. H. Elliott, (Eds.) *The physiology and medicine of diving.* Baltimore: Williams & Wilkins, 1969.

Lanphier, E. H. & Gillen, H. W. Management of sports diving accidents. *New York Journal of Medicine,* 1963, *63,* 667-671.

National Transportation Safety Board Parachute Accident Data. Washington, D. C.: Department of Transportation, September 1967.

Parker, D. W. The hazards of scuba diving. *Canadian Journal of Public Health,* 1965, *56,* 292-296.

Pauley, S. M. & Cockett, A. T. K. Role of lipids in decompression sickness. *Aerospace Medicine,* 1970, *41,* 56-59.

Prasser, D. O. Drowning and hyperventilation syndrome. *California Medicine,* 1969, *111,* 322-324.

Seemann, K. & Wandel, A. Der Taucherunfall mit Uberdehnung der Lunge and Luftembolie (The diving accident with over-distension of the lung and air embolism). *Munchener Medizinische Wochenschrift,* 1967, *109,* 2168-2175.

Skinner, B. F. *Science and human behavior.* New York: Macmillan, 1953.

Strauss, M. & Wright, P. A diving casualty suggesting an episode of thoracic squeeze. U.S. Naval Submarine Medical Center, Groton, Connecticut, 1969, *584.*

Taylor, G. D., Williams, E. H., & Chappell, B. S., Skin and scuba diving fatalities. *Journal of Florida Medical Association.* 1963, *49,* 808-810.

U. S. Navy Diving Manual (NAVSHIPS 250-538) Navy Department, Washington, D. C. 1970.

Waller, J. A., Caplan, P., & Lowe A. Skin and scuba diving as a health problem. California Department of Public Health, Bureau of Occupational Health, Sacramento, 1964.

Webster, D. P. Skin and scuba diving fatalities in the United States. *Public Health Reports, 81,* Vol. 8, August, 1966.

Weltman, G. & Egstrom, G. H. Perceptual narrowing in novice divers. *Human Factors,* 1966, 8, 499-506.

Wolpe, J. The experimental foundations of some new psychotherapeutic methods. in A. J. Bachrach (Ed.), *Experimental foundations of clinical psychology.* New York: Basic Books, 1962.

Wolpe, J. *Psychotherapy by reciprocal inhibition.* Stanford: Stanford University Press, 1958.

REACTION 1
Fourth Session

Capt. Albert R. Behnke
M. C., USN (Retired)
San Francisco, Calif.

The comprehensive analysis of diving behavior by Arthur Bachrach is especially valuable to physicians and others who must now be cognizant of human problems arising from SCUBA and other forms of underwater activity. The underwater environs expose numerous persons daily to imminent danger of drowning in island and littoral waters.

Breath-hold swimming, for example, has produced cardiac arrythmias of serious import and fatalities. In a sense many of these deaths are self-inflicted in that hyperventilation prior to breath-holding delays the urge to breathe. The CO_2 stimulus to break 'apnea' is removed, and alveolar oxygen may decrease to hypoxic levels with resulting loss of consciousness. Pertinent is the observation that exercise raises the swimmer's tolerance to hypercapnia; collapse may supervene with little or no warning.

I have presented a rather elementary technical problem, knowledge of which is required if the physician is to cope with this type of emergency. Equally important is the role of the physician in the exercise of professional administrative leadership. The following questions and comments indicate requirements:

1. In case of accident, who is responsible?
2. Is diving conducted under the supervision of a qualified instructor?
3. Is the SCUBA diver and swimmer physically qualified?
4. Is there an *emergency medical procedure?*
   a. Which outlines specific measures to handle
      Drowning or near-drowning accidents
      Air embolism
      Decompression sickness
   b. Which stipulates lines of communication
      For transportation to a recompression facility
      For obtaining medical assistance
      For recording all phases of an accident
   c. Which outlines resuscitative measures and administration of oxygen
   d. Which provides the names of persons qualified to handle 'On-the-Spot' emergencies

5. Who checks out the diver with reference to *fitness, adequacy of equipment?* Is the diver on any medication which would impair underwater performance? which would affect judgment and orientation?
6. Are systematic records in the form of a *log* kept of all diving activity

NEUROLOGICAL DAMAGE FOLLOWING DECOMPRESSION

Some findings reported by Dr. I. Rozsahegyi of Hungary are of serious concern (from Decompression of Compressed Air Workers in Civil Engineering, ed R. I. McCallum, Oriel Press, Newcastle-Upon Tyne)

Among 179 persons who had suffered from decompression sickness and who could be examined after four years, there could be found sequelae of lesions caused by decompression in 130 cases. In half of these cases the sequelae were serious. The electroencephalographic (EEG) records have revealed pathological changes in two-thirds of 57 persons who had suffered decompression sickness affecting the central nervous system many years ago.

A common experience is psychological change in caisson workers following the above mentioned brain involvement. Men previously calm and self-controlled become impulsive and easily fall into a rage. Good husbands and fathers ill-treated their wives and children. Pathological drunkenness and intolerance to alcohol are common.

Manifest or not lesions of the central nervous system tend to be permanent.

IMPAIRMENT IN DIVERS AND OTHERS SUBJECTED TO ENVIRONMENTAL STRESS

Nitrogen Narcosis: "I found the torpedo room hatch, then went to the starboard rail and forward about 15 feet. At this time thinking became difficult. I started to tie the descending line to the rail and realized that I wasn't accomplishing anything — I had a moment of blankness — was told I was fouled and to get back on the submarine. Got back and faintly remember starting up again and being pulled."

Claustrophobia-Nyctophobia: Although signs of claustrophobia may rarely be manifest under ordinary conditions, weeks and months of confinement may give rise to a series of disturbances that might otherwise remain obscure. If in addition to restriction (submarines), the factor of darkness is added, the combined stresses tend to create an anxiety neurosis.

A suggestion as to a means of eliciting the claustrophobic tendency arose from observations concerning individuals who wore rubber helmets excluding light. One of the susceptible men had a year previously made a heroic deep sea dive but during a subsequent dive, he lost control of his air supply and "blew" to the surface from a depth of 240 feet. This experience seemed to have initiated a latent anxiety neurosis in an otherwise phlegmatic, stoical individual. The *dark helmet* usually tolerated by divers for periods of 15 hours was torn off in about 20 minutes by the subject diver. He appeared to be greatly disturbed and exhibited gross tremors, rapid pulse rate, and somewhat incoherent speech.

Anoxia: The altered emotional behavior to the stress of anoxia induced by breathing mixtures low in oxygen, by simulated altitude ascents in the low pressure chamber or by actual flight in aircraft has long been recognized. The hypoxia test has been employed to exclude individuals who are emotionally unstable. In the low pressure chamber for example, a quiet, reserved, and well-mannered person may suddenly become belligerent and without provocation strike a fellow worker. The altered behavior is similar to the responses associated with ingestion of alcohol or nitrogen at higher pressures. A student diver taken to 200 feet gave the following evaluation of his dive, "I felt a little drunk when I reached the bottom". Although this dive was his first, he concluded, "It was the best dive yet".

That emotional response is not correlated with intelligence may be inferred from the observations of a naval transport pilot concerning a group of distinguished civilian passengers who at 10,000 feet altitude were friendly, jovial, and loquacious; at 12,000 feet without oxygen the mood changed to irritability, belligerency and expression of expletive language. Being an old hand at flying at hypoxic altitudes, the pilot knew what to do. He took his passengers to 14,000 feet and they became quietly drowsy or went to sleep.

The signs of vasomotor collapse, weakness, pallor, sweating, and nausea, are far more prominent in anoxia than in nitrogen narcosis. A distinction must be made between these signs and altered affective behaviour pattern. There is no doubt that purely psychic influences contribute to the vasomotor phenomena and are no more a reaction of anoxia than similar phenomena which follow the insertion of a hypdermic needle at ground level. As a group however, such individuals can be excluded from diving without strict supervision, if their vasomotor responses are abnormal.

Signs and symptoms of deterioration in mentation and mood are outlined in Table 2. Adverse reactions to acute stresses are usually readily discerned. It is the insidious change associated with chronic fatigue which requires vigilant surveillance.

Man is able to adapt to stresses and the stable individual is the one who has a great deal of compensatory reserve. He will be affected by stress but he will compensate by making greater effort. It may be of interest to record simple criteria for selection of the "right" man whether the field be diving, submarine operations, mountaineering, or polar exploration — or fitness for the responsibilities of married life.

Motivation, meaning the ability to see a task through
technical and professional competence
self-discipline, with emotional stability underlined.

TABLE 1

Some guidelines for everyone concerned with underwater safety with regard to human factors

Axiom: The actions of the emotionally aroused individual are unpredictable

Impairments which preclude an individual on any given day from diving -- A check-off list for the supervisor responsible

Intellectual functions	Impairment referrable to somatic systems: system or region	overt	covert	Affective behavior
difficulty in thinking, concentration	cephalic	drowsiness	heavy head, headache	anxiety tension irritability
impaired memory insight, judgment	respira-tory	shortness of breath shallow, rapid breathing	feeling of suffocation	exaggerated fears depression lethargy
fixation of ideas	vasomotor	sweating pallor rapid pulse	weakness	
	cardiac	decreased ability to work rise in diastolic blood pressure	precordial distress	euphoria excitement hilarity pugnacity
	gastric		loss appetite distress nausea	
	intestinal	diarrhea	cramps	
	neuro-muscular	impaired co-ordination tremors speech disorders	fatigue	

TABLE 2

Manifestations of Acute and Chronic Fatigue in Susceptible Men Subjected to Stresses Inherent in Diving and Submarine Operations.

Mentation	Signs	Symptoms	Behavior
Impairment	Drowsiness	Heavy head	Anxiety
Memory	Sleeplessness	Headache	Tension
Insight			Irritability
Judgment	Shortness of breath	Feeling of suffocation	Exaggerated fears
Cerebration			
Concentration	Rapid breathing		Depression
			Apathy
Verbal expression	Poor response to exercise	Precordial distress, pain	Lethargy
Fixation of ideas			Euphoria
	Rise in blood pressure		Excitement
		Weakness	Hilarity
			Pugnacity
	Sweating, pallor,		
	Rapid pulse rate		
		Loss of appetite	
	Diarrhea	Nausea	
		Distress	

REACTION 2
Fourth Session

Michael Greenwood
Hawaii Laboratory
Naval Undersea Center
Kaneohe, Hawaii

A critical review of Bachrach's paper is difficult for me, for I find myself in such agreement with his thesis. I would contend, however, that he has not gone far enough in his recommendations.

I am not convinced of the validity of Webster's statistics on diving accidents, the source of information from which they are drawn being admittedly weak and incomplete. The statistics of accidents with surface swimmers are most dramatic and cause me to be suspicious of the low accident rate in SCUBA Diving. It may be that the fatality index is not the criterion to use. I have been amazed at the number of reported rescues, without any fatalities having occurred, that the Los Angeles County Life Guard association will be called upon to make in the course of a normal week-end. The naivety and the foolhardiness that brings about the need for these rescues are generally based on the individual's overestimation of his ability in the water. Ignorance is bliss, and this blissful state pervades the motivation of most people who on, in or under the water.

Diving, there really isn't that much to it — a regulator, tank, mask and fins, a few rules of thumb (with no clear understanding of the problems or theories involved being necessary) a few simple instructions, possibly picked up from seeing a program on TV; and what more do you really need to go and play SCUBA DUBEE. There are many thousands of people who would class themselves as Scuba divers whose education was along these very lines. Superficially, such people seem to perform well. Ignorance is bliss and they revel in it. There is a large army of people who are convinced that they can dive, and who will continue to do so until an emergency or unexpected situation comes along to shake their tranquility — their shortcoming being that in most instances they are neither prepared academically or physically to face an emergency.

Many people criticize the Navy Diver training programs without really understanding what the Navy is trying to accomplish through the technique that it uses. Their program involves a lot of exercise, a goodly part of which is running, a lot of harassment for poor or unacceptable performance, either in or out of the water (this usually takes the form of pushups), a lot of emergency training, free ascents and a considerable amount of theory, all topped off by a great deal of pride and tradition in diving. I would not defend the Navy's approach as the ideal, but there is something very important which comes out of it, which for obvious reasons is very difficult to effectively duplicate in civilian traning courses, and this is — DISCIPLINE.

In civilian sports diving, there are realities that will always dictate the training of the SCUBA diver. These are economic considerations and the availability of time that people have to go through training courses. I believe that for the best part, the present recognized SCUBA courses do a creditable job, although there tends to be considerable individual difference in the effectiveness of many of the instructors. This is not to say the standards and techniques cannot be improved. I believe there should be an established depth limit to which the SCUBA diver should go. However, a problem with many divers is not one of having them obtain a given level of proficiency to begin with, but of having them maintain that efficiency once they have obtained it. To maintain their certificates, sports divers should be required to effectively re-license themselves by making annual, if not semiannual, requalification dives.

I mentioned that I do not think Bachrach's suggestions went far enough. I believe the real problem or deficiency with the training of divers, lies not so much with the training of the sports diver, as it does with the professional diver.

It does not follow that by giving the sports diver a mission and by paying him for his services that he is thereby a professional diver. Professional diving is more a philosophy or approach to diving. Whereby the craze for sports diving (and that is what it surely is) has probably reached its maximum, the applications and need for professional diving is only just beginning. Scientific and industrial personnel are finding an increasing need and value in going underwater. However, scientists or industrial specialists are scientists or specialists firsts, and divers second. The value of their primary talents are such that it is economically worth the time in taking advantage of all the suggestions that Bachrach oulines, that is, the pacing or shaping of their behavior as divers based on their individual ability and demonstrated performance. The advantages of working with the individual and teaching diving on this basis is no where more clearly demonstrated than by Stewart's program at Scripps. However, professional diving as we know it today, and as we have known it in the past, will be substantially different from the professional diving of the future. Deep diving to six hundred feet and greater, saturation diving, is bound to become fairly commonplace within the scientific and industrial communities. This kind of diving requires equipment and techniques which are several orders of magnitude more complex and demanding than the equipment which the present professional uses. However, notwithstanding the added complexity, the diving of tomorrow will share a common difficulty with the diving of today; it looks easier than it is. They say that ignorance of the law is no defense, and the same argument must surely be true for diving — what you don't know in diving cannot only hurt you, it can kill you, or just as important, it can kill someone else.

Professional diving can be a secondary skill. We are rapidly getting to the point where it will have to become a primary skill, such that the whole equation of what you make out of whom may well have to be changed. If people are going to learn the skills of the professional diver, the new deep professional diver, they must be willing to devote months to their training and not just a couple of weeks.

If we are to minimize accidents in diving, then we must increase disciplined behavior through education, and improve the capability of the amateur by first improving the capability and the training of the professional.

REFERENCE

Bachrach, A.J. *Diving Behavior* (Draft) Naval Medical Research Institute, NNMC, Bethesda, Maryland.

REACTION 3
Fourth Session

Dr. Joseph B. MacInnis
Medical Director
Ocean Systems, Inc.

In his lucid and informative paper Art Bachrach has given us a synoptic view of some of the problems inherent in the behavior of the free-diver. He has noted that we need a term which effectively summarizes the unique vulnerability of the diver. I would like to suggest that we might aptly describe the diver as "an object compressed in space". I would also like to recommend that the many potential and actual stressors acting upon the diver could be described as the "multi-compressions of diving". It is evident that both these descriptive terms are an over simplification — but, simplification is critically important in the learning process. Art Bachrach, as are all of us who teach, is most concerned with this process and its proper evolution.

In his paper, Dr. Bachrach expresses his deep concern about the beginner — his motives — his teaching — and his behavior beneath the sea. I noticed that one question in particular provides an undercurrent to the whole paper . . . and this is — how effective are we in warning the neophyte about the hazards of diving.

I would like to introduce an illustrative method that I believe clarifies the multiple hazards that may stress the diver (Fig. 1). Today we are orbit conscious so let us consider that the diver is surrounded by two orbits of actual and potential events. The inner orbit is made up of those events which act upon the diver as soon as he begins his descent, and remain with him throughout his time underwater. Some of these events center around sensory inputs such as vision, hearing, touch and appreciation of gravity. Other events relate to motor output such as voice and motion of muscles. Other speakers at this meeting have detailed the special effects on man of these altered sensory and motor modalities while he is underwater. I think, however, it is imperative if we are to direct the diving behavior of the student that we tell him of these modalities and that they are (a) distinctly different from those found on land and (b) in most cases unconsciously compensated for by the diver. What I am saying is that most of our students are not aware that their sensory inputs and motor outputs will be greatly changed while underwater and that they will unconsciously compensate for them during the dive. I think that such an understanding would be valuable in the learning process.

The outer orbit of events lists hazards which are *potential only.* Most of those which I have illustrated such as fire, aseptic necrosis, etc. concern only the deep industrial and scientific diver. However, probable events such as thermal instability, and nitrogen narcosis concern the sport diver. The point I want to make is that we need to continually refine and simplify teaching — so that the novice sees at a glance the "multi-compressions of diving".

Let me give you another illustration which is helpful in understanding diving behavior. This simplification is what I call "the diving performance corridor" (Fig 2). In this illustration I have summarized again, only in a different form, the actual and potential stresses of the natural environment, the gaseous environment and the diver himself. A glance indicates that the effective performance of

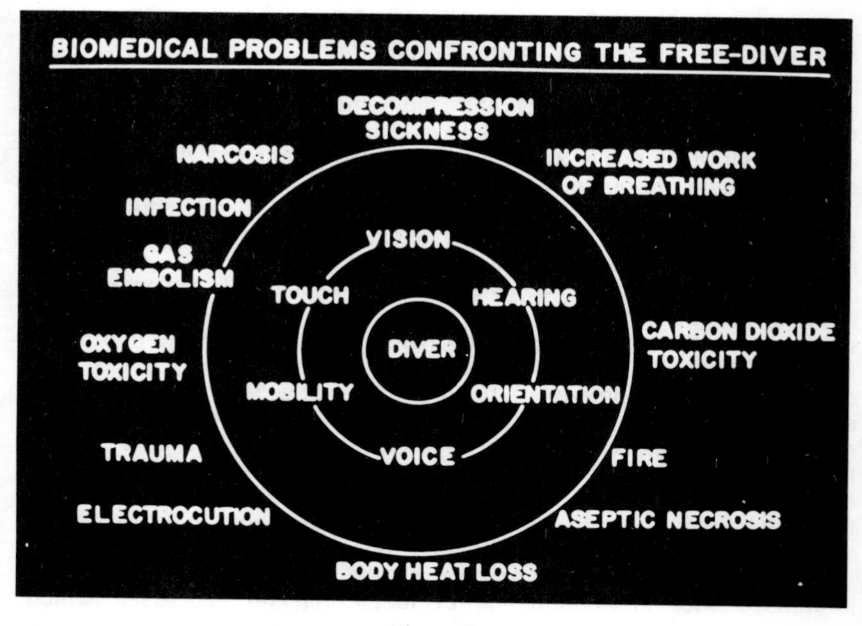

Figure 1

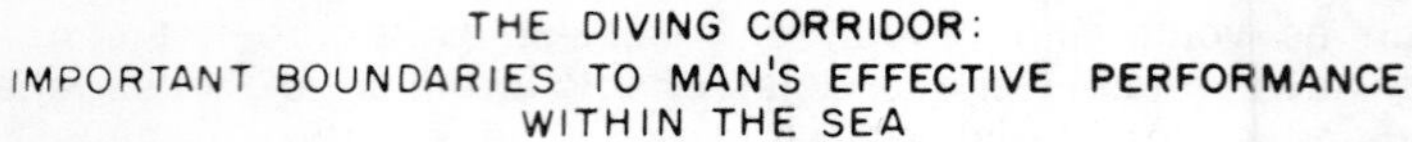

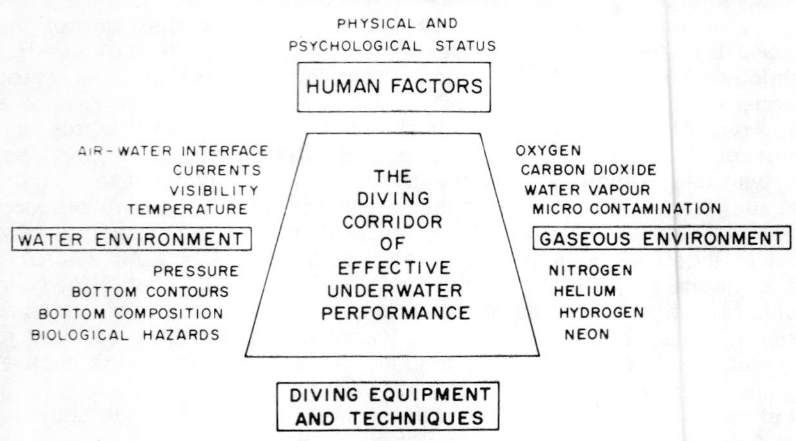

BREATHING DEVICE · THERMAL PROTECTION
COMMUNICATION NAVIGATION · PROPULSION TOOLS
DECOMPRESSION CHAMBERS · DECOMPRESSION SCHEDULE

Figure 2

a diver is constrained by the two walls and ceiling of the corridor. In addition, I should point out that this is a corridor which emphatically narrows with depth. It is supported by a floor — a floor of life-supporting equipment which allows the diver to move within the constraints imposed by the sea, his breathing gas and himself. It is easily apparent that if the equipment is not working or is inadequate to begin with, that the effective performance of a diver is further compressed. These two illustrations, I think, can serve a useful purpose in helping both the teacher and the student to better understand predictable outcomes of diving behavior.

I think I can add some insight to Dr. Bachrach's statement that swimming experience might lead an inexperienced diver to over estimate his ability to assume risks ordinarily not taken. In the mid 50's I was a competitive swimmer (who was suffering from a serious case of pre-Olympic syndrome). I realize now that a learning experience such as diving should logically flow from caution to confidence. It was my mistake to slip rapidly into a phase of over-confidence . . . and I was lucky that I did not get into trouble. This personal experience confirms what Dr. Bachrach has stated and what I too believe . . . that highly experienced swimmers often slip into rapid and irreversible trouble.

While reviewing Dr. Bachrach's paper I could not help but be impressed with the confluence of ideas that he expressed which confirmed some of my own thoughts. Principle among Dr. Bachrach's statements were those pertaining to (a) the majority of diving accidents occurring in less than 50 feet of water; (b) panic and inexperience playing a predominate role; (c) the transition from pool to open water is an extremely difficult step for many students; (d) purposeful work minimizes the potential for anxiety; (e) the proper control of respiration in ascent and descent is perhaps the most important skill to be established in the diver; (f) the hazards of air embolism should be emphasized early in diver training. This is a rather long and weighty list of considerations. Dr. Bachrach has emphasized the importance, and I would like to introduce now a concept which I believe is most effective in the understanding, teaching, training, regarding the above factors.

The concept is the shallow water habitat. For nine months now, I have directed a project in Canada called SUBLIMNOS. SUBLIMNOS is a small, inexpensive habitat located in 30 feet of water close to the shore. Since June of 1969 it has been a focus of research and education. Over 10,000 hours of diving have been logged by approximately 700 visiting students, scientists, and artists. My objective was to explore the scientific and educational opportunities offered by this shallow water habitat. The program has returned its $20,000 investment and much more. I would like to tell you, in great detail, all that we have learned about ourselves and the environment from this unique underwater perspective . . . but let me offer some suggestions relating to Dr. Bachrach's statements.

Sublimnos

First of all, the shallow water habitat offers an excellent location to make a transition from pool to open water. It provides a warm comfortable base and safe refuge. Such a habitat also encourages the stimulus for purposeful work. For example, we have established artificial reefs, experimented with new breathing and thermal protective devices, tested underwater communication booths, conducted "under ice" studies, initiated a survey of the ecosystem of the bay in which we are located, and conducted countless other tasks — using SUBLIMNOS as a base. A habitat is an ideal location for teaching. What better place to discuss the relative merits of controlled respiration during descent and ascent . . . . and the extreme hazards of gas embolism. We know that the majority of diving accidents occur in water that is shallow. It seems to me that it makes sense to establish a habitat where training can take place and an introduction to advanced techniques can be initiated.

I believe that the most of such an installation and the state of technology is such that a university or even a group of diving clubs could establish and operate such a habitat. We have been extremely fortunate in obtaining a research grant from the National Geographic Society. I suggest that there is a great deal to be learned about the environment and about underwater man from a habitat like SUBLIMNOS. For my part I would like to see SUBLIMNOS-type facilities at key locations around this continent. The Great Lakes, the North-East coast, Florida, and California are a few ideal locations. At the same time, we are gaining a better idea of our own diving behavior. We can be gathering knowledge about the new environment in which we swim. As well, we have an opportunity to study the intricate and harmonious web which exists between the diver and his wet world.

Dr. Bachrach's paper has catalytic properties. It tells us rightly that we know little about ourselves and our students during the period of their descent and return to the surface. As a physiologist I know that many of the physiological bariers to shallow diving have been effectively studied and comprehended. What Dr. Bachrach points out is that we still have a long way to go in the comprehension of the behavior of underwater man.

DISCUSSION

Fourth Session

Dr. Bradner: Let me then turn this session over to the panelists for questions and answers. If I may, I'd like to start out by asking, or commenting, that in the second of the panelists' comments — this question of the professional vs. the amateur, I guess, by implication also, vs. the instructor — I've always had a simplified view that the amateur was the one who was diving because he likes the excitement or the thrill, the professionalf was doing it because there's work to be done and diving is the tool, and that the instructor is the one who has to be sure that he doesn't mislead the man for whichever route it is that he wants to follow. Am I oversimplifying dangerously?

Mr. Greenwood: Yes, I believe you are because many amateur divers have tasks that they go underwater to do. One of the problems with diving, with the diving industry and with the whole sort of modern craze of — you know — man in the sea, is a question of what are we putting man in the water to do? Pathetically little, in most cases. This concerns me about the Navy's diving programs because in most of the deep diving that we're interested in pursuing — although academically it's very interesting — pragmatically I think there are other means of accomplishing the same ends which would probably be safer and maybe more economical.

Oh, I'm getting a little bit off the track. A professional diver is really just an amateur diver who thinks a great deal of himself and his ability. I believe, though, that these are really two different types of people. SCUBA diving experience, even a lot of it, doesn't make you a professional diver and even participation in project which has, you know, some underwater work, does not make you a professional diver. Because if we use that criterion, anybody can call himself a professional.

Dr. Bradner: In some other fields you get the label "professional" where you start getting paid for it and perhaps this is an unnecessary. . . .

Dr. Bachrach: I would say that Glen said yesterday . . . I like to use quotes a lot — there's one I enjoy that I don't get a chance to use very often. Diving may be in the same position that Bernard Shaw said that prostitution was in danger of being ruined by amateurs.

Dr. Bradner: Were there some of written remarks or questions?

Dr. Bachrach: There seems to be a cluster of several which are related, which we might take up as one, a question regarding the training for controlled ascent. Several questions dealt with this. Should there be recompression chambers, is there any necessity for making it mandatory, and so on? I might kick off by saying that I feel that a controlled, emergency ascent dive is essential. Perhaps Dr. Behnke might comment on whether or not the dangers involved require the availability of a recompression chamber. It seems to me that if we accept what I believe is the fact that the ascent period is the most dangerous, then I certainly feel that training for emergency ascent with the regulator held in hand as is commonly done, the airway clear with the head back, and so on, I think this is a skill of response that is absolutely essential for effective and safe diving.

Capt. Behnke: Oh, I don't think there's any question about the training in the free ascent under proper conditions. In other words, all of the SCUBA divers should have their training to be able to ascend without a device from 60 feet without any trouble. This is no problem. It's a little training — that's what it takes.

Now, I don't want to get on the old subject again, except to emphasize the most critical need today is a recompression chamber wherever there's diving. Mr. Reedman will follow-up, I think, in a paper and perhaps a summary or part of it could be in the Proceedings dealing with the simplicity of finding today a small, economical chamber. A small chamber for two people with the oxygen therapy that's available on the assumption that individuals will be recompressed and treated immediately. These chambers can be run by you people. You don't have to have a doctor. An M.D. probably knows generally less about it than you do. You can operate it. If you can't turn a valve or two, you're not doing your job. You shouldn't be here. There's nothing to it. You have anything to add to this?

Dr. MacInnis: Yeah. I'd like to comment that although most of our work is done in less than 30 feet of water, we're installing a chamber at the site and that, once we have it, we will be doing ascent training.

Dr. Bachrach: Well, I have a comment here that, which has been made many, many times. I really feel a necessity for underscoring or or footnoting; I'm a little more anxious about operating a chamber. I think fire hazards are something that are always there and I think it isn't any more possible for *anyone* to operate a chamber than anyone to dive. I'm not sure that we're all aware of it, but the number of fires in chambers that could occur are frightening. I think that I would like to footnote that as something to consider — *not to take chamber operation too lightly!*

Audience quesion: Do we need a scientist in the water to operate the new equipment?

Mr. Greenwood: You're right. But maybe we don't need the scientist in the water. Maybe we can make very efficient scientific technicians out of the divers because I think the physical requirements and the amount of time that is going to be necessary to become proficient in the types of equipment that'll be used will be more than the busy scientist is going to be able to devote going into the water. If he wants to go there, he's probably going to have to go in a submersible, look through a porthole and maybe leave the scubie-dubie role to somebody else that can train effectively as a technician.

Dr. MacInnis: I disagree with you, Mike.

Audience question: Are you saying that anyone can be trained as a scientific observer to do scientific studies?

Mr. Greenwood: No, I'm not saying that. I'm saying that right now we can possibly train just about anybody to dive with relative degrees of proficiency in a two or three-week time period, and get him into the water to do the type of scientific studies that a lot of people are interested in. We're not going to be able to train just anybody, I think, in the future. So that it might, in most cases, be easier to train people as scientific technicians from a psychiatry of real, professional divers. Maybe I'm talking about another kind of diving. I'm talking about my own sort of interests in saturation diving and very deep diving. We're talking of types of equipment that people have to live in pretty much all the time where the upkeep and the maintenance is a full-time job. It isn't something you sort of breeze down to the docks in the morning, pick up, and go out to sea with. I'm saying that diving cannot, I think, in the future continue as a secondary skill if we're going to push diving to its ultimate end. It will have to be a primary skill and the question will be: will the researcher be willing to make it a primary skill and give it equal time with his other interests? I think, in many cases, the answer will be "no" so that he will have to go and train the diver as a scientific technician to do some of his tasks underwater for him.

Dr. MacInnis: I don't agree with you, Mike.

Mr. Greenwood: You don't?

Dr. MacInnis: It should be more scientist. . . .

Audience question: Can hyperventilation extend the free diver's ability to stay under water?

Dr. Egstrom: I'm concerned with hyperventilation used as a tool for extending free divers' ability to stay down as opposed to inadvertent hyperventilation. Now, could we be concerned with two things here and maybe label one deliberate and another inadventent because I think we're talking about two different things.

Dr. Bachrach: I think the hazards, though, are the same in both cases.

Dr. Egstrom: Granted.

Dr. Bachrach: I think that hyperventilation to stay down can still reduce the carbonic acid levels — CO_2 — to a point of hazard. I think you can also get intrathoracic pressure. The hyperventilation on the surface which is a different one, as you say, is associated more with a panic than a deliberate kind of a technique. But I feel that the diver who free dives and hyperventilates in order to give himself more air may also be running the risk of this CO_2 problem. I think it's always hazardous.

Audience question: I would like a point of clarification from Dr. Bachrach. He mentioned the stress and I've certainly come to some conclusions that there really is some correlation between ways of measuring stress between one way and another way and also individuals can react to stress. So, what I would like to know is if there's some way you can clarify or maybe give us some indications of a true reactive way of measuring stress in diving situations.

Dr. Bachrach: Perhaps Glen might want to comment on that. I think this is a real knotty one, that I don't feel very comfortable with the measurements of stress that we have now to be sure. We can get pretty accurate measurements of heart rate, pulse rate, and so on. Here again, as you indicate, stress is in part a large measure of learned phenomenon. I think someone was telling me that Scott Crossfield on take off in the X-15 was running rates up in the 170-180 on take off and yet was perfectly competent to handle the thing. Now, this is another aspect of stress, whether an individual is stressed and coping.

The measures we have are primarily such things as respiration rates, heart rates, and so on and they are not entirely accurate. I think that one of the tasks to which our own labs will be addressed will be the accurate measurement of behavioral physiological change. We're quite conscious of this, I would agree. The learned aspect is one of the more interesting things. As I mentioned, I think that learning to cope with stress is largely a function of increments of self confidence and control.

Audience question: We've talked an awful lot about the psychological effects on the diver, and I'm kind of concerned with the psychological effects of the researcher.

Dr. Bachrach: It seems to me that as a scientist I can dive if I want to but that the skills of the scientist and those of the diver should mesh. The diver should *not* be used as a tool, as an exploited experimental subject. I wonder if it shouldn't be realized that in order to achieve effective communication and everything, the guy who goes through all this training, do a specific thing, and live in an environment that's not normal should be considered as an equal.

Dr. MacInnes: I'd like to comment that we ran into that problem with Ocean Systems. We would bring divers up from the Gulf of Mexico or Santa Barbara to Navy dive, the paperwork would be fantastic and so they discourage me from this because I'm over-age in the twilight of my years. But, I think that your point ought to be reemphasized; that too often we have treated the divers as subjects instead of co-equals. One of the things that we've been doing especially with Ken's help is to sit down to talk to divers about the kinds of questions they want to know about. I did this the summer before last, and I had the chance to work with Mike and some of the others on SEALAB. If I might just summarize quickly what they wanted to know. It struck me as being interesting. *They were interested in oxygen toxicity, nitrogen narcosis, and equipment, primarily. These were the things, and of course cold. If you focus upon all of these problems, what they were saying in effect was, help me with the things which I cannot control because if I lose control, then I'm through.* And I think that what it amounts to in this profession, is that they assume that they have the confidence to handle the job, given a job to do underwater. But if they lose control — like getting bitten by a scorpion fish or having a convulsion from oxygen or narcosis — they are no longer the coping, competent individual that they consider themselves to be. This is the kind of question that the professional, the SEALAB-type divers, are asking and I think they are reasonable.

Dr. Bradner: I'd like to make a couple of final announcements. Then if there's anybody that I cut short from an urgent question that doesn't have to do with diving, break in.

First, there was a great problem yesterday of getting copies of Navy diving papers and an arrangement will be made to get those as quickly as we can through The Athletic Institute. In the normal course of events, then, they would come out with the Proceedings of the Symposium.

I think it's the appropriate time now, then, to thank The Athletic Institute and Scripps Institution of Oceanography but also, especially, the speakers and the organizers of this Symposium. It has been extremely valuable, the comments that everybody has made, and let us just — for those who are within earshot — give a vote of thanks right now. For those of you, then, who wish to spend the next hour informally discussing instruction with special reference to diving accidents, are invited to stay here, but the formal Symposium is now then terminated.

Appendix[1]

DIVER ONE- AND TWO-ARM STRENGTH TESTS[2]

SUMMARY

A series of one- and two-arm diver strength tests were conducted to obtain data basic for the optimum design of underwater tools. Measurements were made with divers working on vertical, overhead, and deck like surfaces where no natural handholds or footholds existed. Tethering equipment was used for diver restraint during the two-arm tests. Obtained diver force data ranged from 17.5 to 35.4 pounds for the one-arm tests and 32.3 to 80.4 pounds for two arms with tethering. Recommendations are made for modes of tool design which may increase productivity and/or reduce the requirements for sustained diver thrust.

INTRODUCTION

The strength measurements were made to obtain basic data which could serve as a guide for designers of underwater power tools. Test equipment representative of actual tools and work surfaces and realistic work positions and durations were used to increase the validity of the tests for the stated purpose.

The tests were conducted jointly by the Naval Civil Engineering Laboratory, Port Hueneme, and the Naval Missile Center, Point Mugu, California. The study was sponsored by the Naval Facilities Engineering Command.

TEST EQUIPMENT

A hand dynamometer was constructed of corrosion-resistant components (Figure D-1). The dynamometer was configured to resemble an underwater power-tool motor with realistic weight and balance. Calibration was accomplished with the dynamometer in the horizontal position. The instrument measures thrust up to 100 pounds.

[1] Appendix to paper of John T. Quirk. See page 107.

[2] Diver Performance Using Handtools and Hand-Held Pneumatic Tools Technical Report R 653 Naval Civil Engineering Laboratory

Figure D-1. Hand dynamometer.

The ocean test structure (Figure D-2) consisted basically of two 6 x 12-foot steel plates, one mounted in the vertical plane and the other in the horizontal. The plates were mounted on a welded pipe framework. Hydraulic jetting was used to embed the three legs of the framework into the ocean bottom (sand).

The diver-tethering equipment consisted of a tethering jacket, quick-release adjustable straps, and magnets and suction cups as shown in Figure D-3.

An underwater timer and data board (Figure D-4) was used by the test conductor.

Figure D-2. Ocean test structure.

TEST METHODS

Three NCEL civilian engineers and four Naval Construction Battalion enlisted men served as test subjects. All were Navy certified divers in good physical condition.

The test subjects were instructed as to the purpose of the tests and asked to apply forces they would consider reasonable if they were using power tools underwater in contrast to participating in a competitive strength contest.

The tests were conducted in the ocean at a depth of 50 feet. Water temperatures varied from 54°F to 58°F. Measurements were made with the divers working on three different work surfaces—vertical, overhead and deck—which were designed to be representative of ship surfaces.

The one-arm tests were made with the divers holding onto a suction cup handle with one hand and pressing against the test plate holding the dynamometer in the preferred hand. During the two-arm tests, the divers wore tethering jackets, and attached the quick-release straps to suction

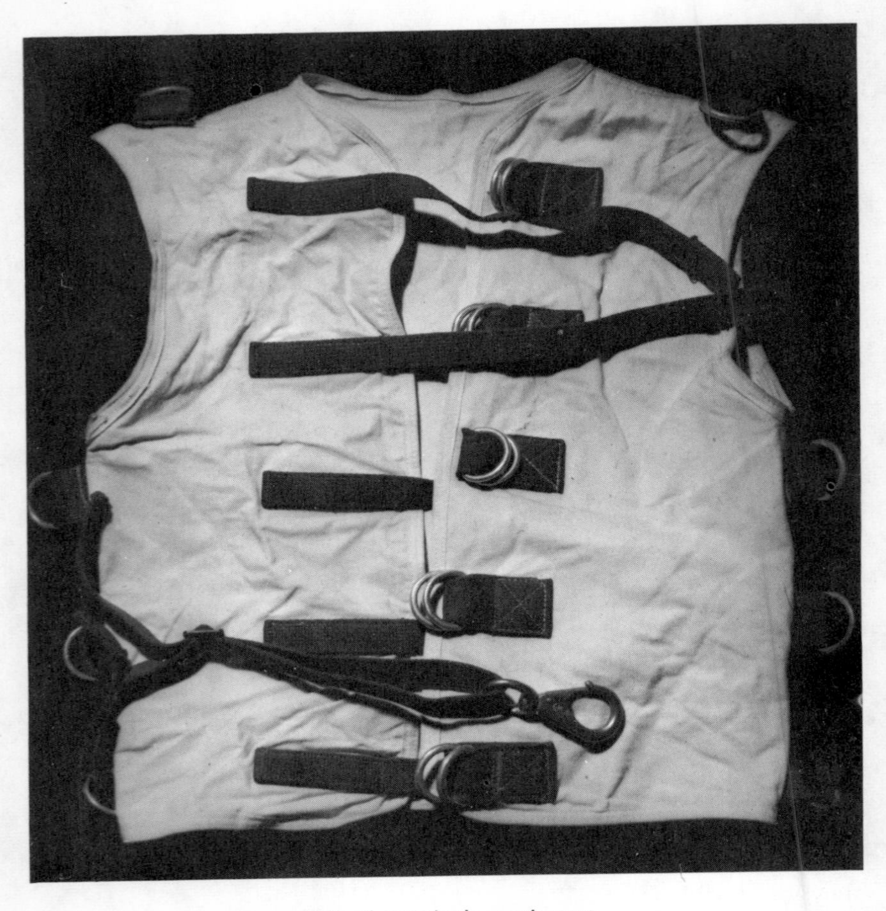

Figure D-3. Diver tethering equipment.

cups, magnets, or eye bolts, as preferred. They held the dynamometer with both hands. The three work durations were six minutes, three minutes and one minute.

Since it was not possible to measure and record force continuously during any given trial, discrete measurements were made during each trial and averaged. Six measurements were made at 1-minute intervals for the six-minute trials; three measurements were at 1-minute intervals for the three-minute trials; and four measurements were made at 15-second intervals for the one-minute trials. The test conductor could observe the

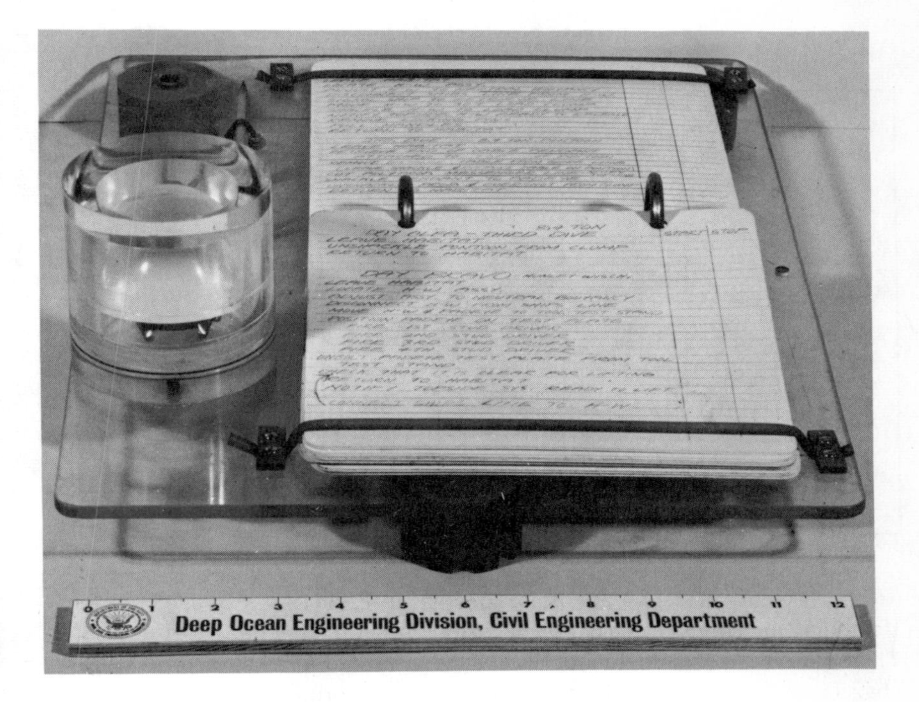

Figure D-4. Underwater timer and data board.

dynamometer pointer at all times and attempted to record mean force measurements for each interval. This was necessary due to the inability of some divers to maintain nearly constant force.

All of the work for a given surface was done on one and sometimes two dives for each subject. The order of conditions (that is, one or two arms; 6-, 3-, or 1-minute duration; and vertical, overhead, or deck surface) was varied at random from subject to subject. Subjects were informed of the duration of each trial in advance so that they might pace themselves appropriately. Each of the seven subjects for whom data is reported were tested for all 18 conditions of the experiment.

RESULTS

The average results for all subjects are presented in Table D-1. These values have been corrected for the weight of the dynamometer. The weight was added to the measured overhead forces and subtracted from the deck forces.

Table D-1. Average Diver Force Data

Work Surface	No. of Arms	Diver Force (lb) for Duration of—			Mean Diver Force (lb)	
		6 Minutes	3 Minutes	1 Minute	Each Arm	Both Arms
Overhead	one	18.8	21.4	29.0	23.1	35.5
	two	32.3	38.9	72.9	48.0	
Vertical	one	21.8	23.6	34.5	26.6	36.6
	two	35.7	41.4	62.6	46.6	
Deck	one	17.5	18.4	35.4	23.8	39.6
	two	42.2	44.0	80.4	55.5	
Mean	one	19.3	21.1	32.9	24.5	–
	two	36.7	41.4	71.9	50.0	–
	both	28.0	31.2	52.4	–	37.2

Several interesting trends are apparent in Table D-1. For all conditions there is an increase in force with a decrease in the time the force was applied. There is also a less marked tendency for the measured force to increase with changes in direction of application from overhead, through vertical, to deck.

Approximate diver force curves for the different conditions are illustrated in Figure D-5. The curves were "splined in" from the three calculated data points for each, and may be used for obtaining estimates of diver force for the other listed time intervals. The curves were not extended beyond six minutes as this is a very long time to apply constant force. Longer durations would be exceptionally difficult for the divers and are not considered practical.

Table D-2 lists the highest and lowest mean forces measured for individual divers for the different time and arm conditions.

Table D-2. Force Measurement Ranges

(Based on individual diver mean scores.)

No. of Arms	Test Range	Diver Force (lb) for Duration of—		
		6 Minutes	3 Minutes	1 Minute
two	high	50.0	61.3	102.5
	low	13.0	22.7	28.3
one	high	32.3	33.3	54.0
	low	8.8	12.0	20.8

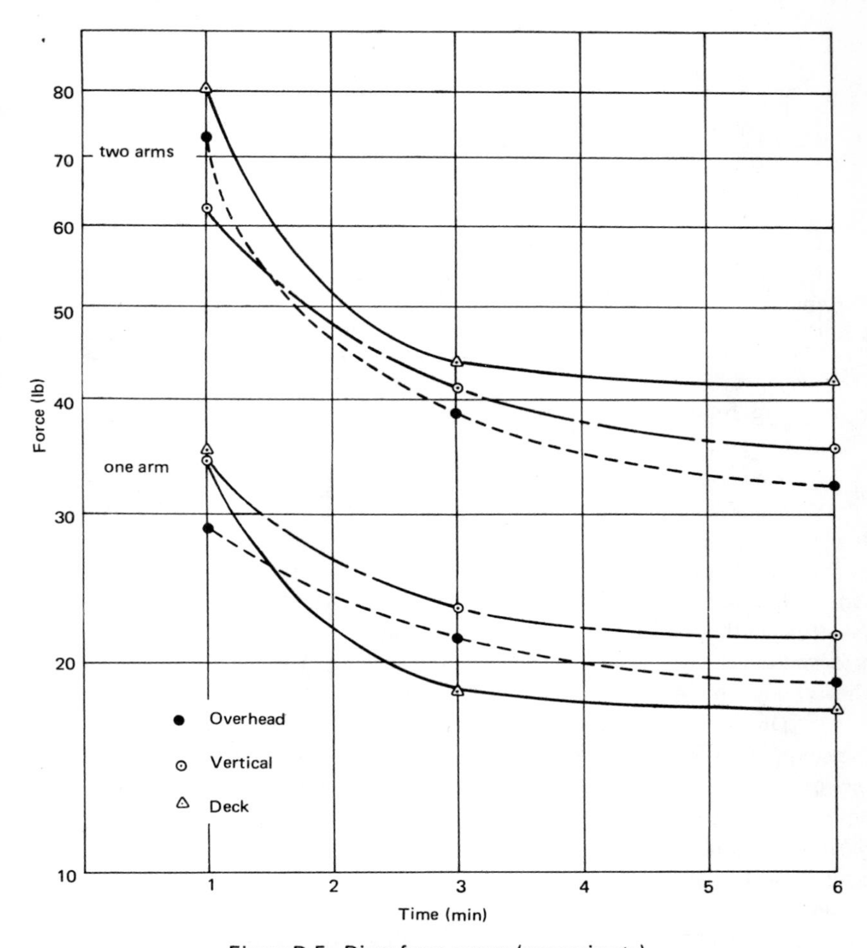

Figure D-5. Diver force curves (approximate).

The statistical significance levels of the obtained comparisons are listed in Table D-3.

The sign method of statistical analysis was used for comparison of arm and time conditions. Analysis of variance (computed separately for each time and arm condition) was used for comparison of the position conditions.

Table D-3. Statistical Significance

Comparison	Significance Level
One arm versus two arms	0.01
One minute versus three and six minutes	0.01
Three minutes versus six minutes	0.05
Deck versus vertical and overhead	NS
Vertical versus overhead	NS

CONCLUSIONS AND RECOMMENDATIONS

The approximate doubling of applied force resulting from the use of tethering equipment is a strong indication of the importance of providing a restraining support for the diver.

Divers on occasion will be able to stand on a platform or the seafloor, where they can thrust forward with their legs and trunk to obtain greater pressure on the tool in use. Although beyond the scope of the subject tests, this method of working should also be investigated. We can assume, however, that some increase in thrust will result.

Diver force can be expected to vary under the test conditions from approximately 30 pounds to over 100 pounds for a 1-minute, two-arm operation and from 9 to 33 pounds for a 6-minute, one-arm operation. The amount of force applied will largely depend on the strength of the diver. Since optimum cutting speed is partially a function of pressure exerted against the tool bit, it may be necessary to provide variable tool speed to obtain maximum cutting rates for all conditions.

The divers found it very uncomfortable and sometimes painful to apply maximum thrust for the six-minute interval. As on land, it would much ease the burden on the worker and increase productivity if some mechanical assistance could be obtained to apply the required force.

Impacting is an excellent example of another successful mode of reducing the counterthrust required by the worker. Another solution, the use of high-speed rotary cutting blades, has been thoroughly demonstrated by land tools and is possibly suitable for underwater use.

UNDERWATER PHYSIOLOGY SYMPOSIUM
La Jolla, California
April 10-11, 1970

Speakers

Dr. Arthur Bachrach
Director, Behavioral Sciences Department
Naval Medical Research Institute, NNMC
Bethesda, Maryland

Dr. Glen Egstrom
Department of Physical Education
University of California
Los Angeles

CDR. Bob Hoke, MC, USN
Naval Medical Research Institute
National Naval Medical Center
Bethesda, Maryland

Dr. Gershon Weltman
Bio-Technology Laboratory
Department of Engineering
University of California
Los Angeles

Panelists

Captain Albert Behnke, MC, USN, (Ret)
University of California Medical Center

CDR. Robert Bornmann, MC, USN
Deputy Assistant for Medical Affects
Deep Submergence Systems Project Office
Chevy Chase, Maryland

Dr. Hugh Bowen
Dunlap and Associates, Inc.
Darien, Connecticut

Dr. Mark Bradley
Deep Submergence Systems Project Technical Office
San Diego, California

Mike Greenwood
Naval Undersea Research and Development Center
Kailua, Hawaii

Dr. Joseph MacInnis
Medical Director
Ocean Systems Inc.
Toronto, Canada

Bev Morgan
Deep Water Development Corp.
Goleta, California

John T. Quirk
Naval Civil Electronics Laboratory
Port Hueneme, California

James R. Stewart, Diving Officer
Scripps Institute of Oceanography
La Jolla, California

Lt. CDR. Tommy Thompson, USN (Ret)
U. S. Divers Corporation
Santa Ana, California

Dr. William Vaughn
President, Oceanautics Inc.
Alexandria, Virginia

Lt. CDR. James Vorosmarti
Deep Submergence Systems Project Technical Office
San Diego, California

Symposium Planning Committee

Dr. Ted Forbes, Chairman
University of California
San Diego

Dr. Edmund Bernauer
University of California
Davis

Dr. Glen H. Egstrom
University of California
Los Angeles

Charles Jehle
AMF Voit, Inc.
Santa Ana

Dr. Frank B. Jones
The Athletic Institute
Chicago

James R. Stewart
Scripps Institute of
Oceanography
La Jolla

Participants

Patrick William Albin
San Francisco State College

Barbara Allen
Westinghouse Ocean Research
Laboratory
San Diego, California

Richard A. Ames
Santa Ana City College

Michael G. Amsbry
AMF Voit, Inc.
Santa Ana, California

Ada B. Anderson
Technitron, Inc.
Falls Church, Virginia

Roger Anderson
Deputy, Sheriff's Department
County of Los Angeles

Lloyd Austin
University of California, Berkeley

Philip R. Austin
Bethlehem YMCA
Bethlehem, Pennsylvania

Robert B. Banzett
University of California, Davis

Steven W. Barnett
Cupertino High School
Campbell, California

Arthur A. Basham
San Jose State College

Satch W. Baumgart
Technitron
Reston, Virginia

Rene M. Beaumont
Beckman Instruments Inc.
Laguna Niguel, California

Art Beck
San Diego, California

Dallas B. Boggs
Ocean Ventures Industries
Coronado, California

Brian C. Borgh
NAUI
Santa Barbara, California

Robert P. Bradley
International Hydrodynamics
Vancouver. B. C.

Robert Brennan
Santa Ana College

Judy Brennan
Santa Ana College

Charles F. Breslin
Litton Systems, Inc.
Los Angeles, California

Michael A. Brick
Scuba Technology Institute
Los Angeles, California

Michael T. Brophy
San Diego, California

Margaret B. Butterfield
NAUI
Chula Vista, California

Dennis Carey
Dana Point, California

Deane R. Carlson
San Diego, California

Mitchell Vincent Casteel
Santa Ana College

Audrey Comeau
Santa Ana College

Skip C. Conner
Corona del Mar, California

Skip C. Conner, (Mrs.)
Corona del Mar, California

M. Kam Cooney
Mission Hills, California

Leon J. Corcoran
Hydro Products, Divn. of
Dillingham Corp.
San Diego, California

Raymond J. Cormier
San Diego Downtown YMCA
Lemon Grove, California

Richard P. Cramer
Men's Physical Education
Department
Oregon State University

William J. Cuccaro
UCLA

John S. Curtin
Downtown YMCA
Coronado, California

Bonnie June Davis
L. A. County NAUI
Los Angeles, California

Douglas R. Dawkins
Douglas Aquatics
San Bruno, California

Donald J. DeTata
Scuba Technology Institute
Santa Monica, California

Dora Dickson
Physical Department
Crescenta-Canada Family YMCA
La Canada, California

Carl Ehret
University of California, Davis

John B. Elliot
Santa Ana College

Robert V. Erilane
Los Angeles, California

David E. Farlow
Gresham, Oregon

Darwin R. Ferrin
Marina, California

Verna A. Ferrin
Marina, California

Don D. Flickinger
Consultant, U. S. Air Force
Washington, D. C.

Lawrence J. Folinsbee
University of California, Davis

W. M. Fooshee
NAUI
Chula Vista, California

John Thomas Foster
Sunset Beach, California

John S. Frederick
Scuba Technology Institute
W. Los Angeles, California

Morris J. Fruitman
City of San Mateo, California

Rita L. Fruitman
City of San Mateo, California

Jacquie Gallardo
Inglewood, California

Otto F. W. Gasser
California State Poly College -
Pomona

Barbara A. Gimbel
Torrance South High School
Torrance, California

John O. Gimbel
Greater Los Angeles Council of Divers
Torrance, California

Irv Glushenko
L. A. Underwater Instructors Association
Portuguese Bend, California

Jeff S. Gomes
Fullerton Junior College

Thomas A. Gould
Ross-Loos Medical Group
Los Angeles, California

George T. Green
Ocean Ventures Industries
Coronado, California

Fred H. Hammond
Physical Education Department
San Diego State College

Russell S. Hanson
Mesa College

Stan Harada
Phoenix College

Jon S. Hardy
NAUI
Santa Barbara, California

Robert J. Havle
UNIVAC, Sperry Rand Corp.
Camarillo, California

Bobbi Lynn Haughton
Los Angeles, California

M. Richard Hegeman
General Motors AC Electronics Research Labs
Goleta, California

Lt. William Hemming, USN
Ocean Ventures Industries
Coronado, California

Walter Hetz
Redondo Beach, California

Richard F. Hoe
Technitron, Inc.
Falls Church, Virginia

Ronald G. Homuth
Scuba Technology Institute
Long Beach, California

CDR. Donald Hubbard, USN (Ret)
Ocean Ventures Industries
Coronado, California

Nicholas L. Icorn
U. S. Divers Corp.
Lakewood, California

James E. Innis
Santa Ana College

Boris Innocenti
Phoenix, Arizona

Albert M. Irwin
Physical Education Department
University of California

Charles J. Jehle
AMF Voit, Inc.
Santa Ana, California

Jonathan C. Jones
Fullerton Junior College

Stanley W. Judge
Camarillo, California

Edward F. Kelly
NAUI
Hayward, California

Paul R. Kenis
Naval Undersea R-D Center
Pasadena, California

Carl E. Klafs
California State College, Long Beach

Harry W. Kuller
Tucson, Arizona

Arthur F. Lambert
Saratoga, California

Francis H. Leach
University of California, Santa Cruz

Paul Leiter
Reseda, California

S. R. Leonard
Santa Ana, California

Charles Lesniak, Jr.
New Mexico State University

Jerome W. Levin
Mesa College

Kenneth J. Lindeman
San Diego State College

Bob A. Lubo
Garden Grove Unified School District
Huntington Beach, California

Joan Lyon
California State College at Long Beach

John W. Manlove
Divers Institute of Technology Inc.
Seattle, Washington

Alan P. Mark
Scuba Technology
Inglewood, California

Coralee E. Marical
Costa Mesa, California

Roger Martin
YMCA
San Diego, California

Harold M. McCall
Aerojet General Corp.
Glendora, California

James L. McMillan
Portland, Oregon

Samuel Miller
Garden Grove, California

Michael Minore
Deputy, Sheriff's Department
Los Angeles, California

Chappell B. Moore
Hospital of the Good Samaritan Medical Center
Los Angeles, California

William E. Moritz
Naval Medical Research Int.
Bethesda, Maryland

Donald M. Morrison
Torrance, California

Dennis Hayes Murphy
Fullerton Junior College

Alex P. Nalezinski
San Jose City College

Paul Nardin
El Segundo, California

Muriel Greenwood
El Segundo, California

Robert A. Nelson
Naval Undersea Research & Development Center
La Mesa, California

Vincent S. O'Hara
Fresno, California

Clifford Olds
San Diego City College

Bill N. Oliver
U.S. Divers Company
Huntington Beach, California

Wm. L. Orris
Marine Physician, SIO-UCSD
San Diego, California

John F. Ostarello
Hayward, California

Greg Page
University of California, Berkeley

James S. Parnell
Garden Grove, California

Thomas D. Patrick
Costa Mesa, California

Don S. Peterson
Rogersville, Missouri

Robert W. Peterson
Chula Vista, California

Billie Louise Poston
Fresno State College

Tommy G. Prince
NAUI
Imperial Beach, California

Dr. Harold W. Puffer
University of Southern California

John Reseck, Jr.
Santa Ana College

Dr. George D. Ramsay
San Jose, California

Marilyn M. Rawlings
Kerckhoff Marine Laboratory
Venice, California

Marion K. Reed
San Francisco State College

Robert F. Richardson
Scuba Inc.
Houston, Texas

Fred L. Riedman
Long Beach, California

Richard M. Riedman
San Diego State College

CDR. W. A. Robinson
CSO, Nav SpecWarGru Pac,
Coronado, California

John C. Roodenburg
TRW Sea Divers and GLACD
Lomita, California

Lynn M. Rosenthal
L.A. County U/W Instructor

Reynold J. Ruppe
Department of Anthropology
Arizona State University

Frank J. Scalli
National YMCA
Gloucester, Massachusetts

Gary Schiller
La Jolla, California

Ambrose Schindler
Redondo Beach, California

Lawrence L. Schmelzer
University of California

Marlene P. Schultz
La Canada, Calfiornia

Robert D. Scoles
Manhattan Beach, California

Isaac Sharon
Los Angeles, California

Frank S. Shipp, Sr.
US Naval Oceanographic Office
San Diego, California

James D. Skweres
San Diego City College

James R. Smith
Stanford University

Bart B. Sokolow
UCLA Biotechnology Lab
Los Angeles, California

Lloyd S. Sorensen
General Motors AC Electronics
Research Labs
Goleta, California

C. Merle Sprock
University of California, Davis

John R. Stearns
L.A. County Instructor
Manhattan Beach, California

Helen M. Stearns
L.A. County Instructor
Manhattan Beach, California

James Steele
Steele's Diving Supplies
Oakland, California

Claudia Steele
Steele's Diving Supplies
Oakland, California

James P. Stevenson
Ocean Ventures Industries
Coronado, California

Henry O. Stinnett
Davis, California

Ralph E. Stolz
Allentown Osteopathic Hospital
Emmaus, Pennsylvania

Michael B. Strauss
Comnavspecwargru Pacific
USNAB Coronado
San Diego, California

Dwight Sutton
Regional Primate Research
Center
University of Washington

John Swider
Oceanautics, Inc.
Alexandria, Virginia

Craig Swolgaard
Carmichael, California

Algis G. Taruski
Hospital of the Good Samaritan
Medical Center
Los Angeles, California

Patricia A. Taruski
UCLA

Pat H. Thaxton
Long Beach, California

Nancy M. Thille
L.A. City Board of Education
Agoura, California

F. L. Tinkham
Phoenix College

Raymond H. Thornton
Physical Education Department
University of California

Mrs. Donald G. Tibbetts
Santa Ana College

Donald G. Tibbetts
Santa Ana College

Hal Titus
IGPP
University of Cailfornia,
San Diego

Robert D. Trent
The Fluor Corp., Ltd.
Thousand Oaks, California

Sheila L. Trotter
San Jose City College

Arthur H. Ullrich
NAUI
Colton, California

William W. Van Atta
Pacific Support Group
Naval Oceanographic Office
San Diego, California

Ronald E. Veelik
San Bernardino Valley College

Wm. Laughlin Vetter
UCLA

Paul D. Wakefield
Santa Ana College

James F. Wakeman
TRW Systems
Manhattan Beach, California

Lee A. Walton
San Jose State College

Joseph Turner Watson
L.A. County Underwater
Instructor
La Canada, California
Dave G. Watt

Catalina Island School for Boys
Avalon, California

Robert L. Watts
Naval Undersea R & D Center
San Diego, California

Dick Weaver
Manhattan Beach, California

Dean J. Westgaard
Orange Coast College

Bruce E. Wiggins
NAUI
Oceanside, California

Nancy G. Wiggins
Oceanside, California

CDR. J. B. Williams, USN
NAUI
Chula Vista, California

R. R. Williams
Glendale, Arizona

Donald B. Willis
San Jose City College

John M. Workman
Hospital of the Good Samaritan
Medical Center
Los Angeles, California

John Wozny
Long Beach, California

Douglas G. Wright
Coronav Divers
Coronado, California

Larry Cushman
Chatsworth, California

Francis Kaaren
North Hollywood, California

Darlene Hubbard
Ocean Ventures Industries
Coronado, California

Michael L. J. Lockey
University of California, Berkeley

Tony L. Kobylsk
San Clemente, California

Leland G. Moler
Long Beach, California

Lisa Smith
San Diego, California

Joe Steinmeyer
Anaheim, California

Joe S. Warner
Environmental Health & Safety
University of California,
San Diego

Charles Micone
Environmental Health & Safety
University of California,
San Diego